Dr Brenda Lintner, MRCP (Ed), DPM FRCPsych, has specialised in psychiatry for over thirty years, working particularly with people with schizophrenic illness. She has undertaken research and written several books about psychiatric illness, and has lectured extensively in Britain and Canada.

As Consultant Psychiatrist to Runwell Hospital and the Southend Group of Hospitals, she was involved in the establishment of a community clinic for psychiatric patients, and was advisor to the local branches of the National Schizophrenia Fellowship and Cruse. She was also a member of the Mental Health Review Tribunal, and has recently been elected Fellow of the Royal College of Psychiatry.

Dr Lintner is committed to informing health professionals and the general public about schizophrenia, and dispelling the myths and prejudices which surround this distressing condition.

LIVING WITH SCHIZOPHRENIA

A GUIDE FOR PATIENTS AND RELATIVES

Dr Brenda Lintner
MRCP (Ed), DPM FRCPsych

POSITIVE HEALTH GUIDE

© Brenda Lintner 1989

First published in 1989 by
Macdonald Optima, a division of
Macdonald & Co. (Publishers) Ltd

A member of Maxwell Pergamon Publishing Corporation plc

British Library Cataloguing in Publication Data
Lintner, Brenda
  Living with schizophrenia.
  1. Man. Schizophrenia – For families of
  schizophrenics
  I. Title
  616.89'82

ISBN 0-356-15446-7

Macdonald & Co. (Publishers) Ltd
66–73 Shoe Lane
London EC4P 4AB

Photoset in Times by ✒ Tek Art Ltd

Printed and bound in Great Britain by
Mackays of Chatham PLC, Letchworth

CONTENTS

	Acknowledgements	vii
	Introduction	1
1	A brief history	5
2	What is schizophrenia?	11
3	What causes schizophrenia?	27
4	Recognising schizophrenia	39
5	Planning the treatment of schizophrenia	45
6	Treating schizophrenia	57
7	Community care	85
8	A guide to the benefit system	93
9	Living with schizophrenia	101
10	Legal matters	119
11	Schizophrenia in art and literature	127
12	The future	133
	Glossary	135
	Useful addresses	139
	Further reading	143
	Index	145

ACKNOWLEDGEMENTS

The author would like to express her appreciation to her husband Dr Jiri Lintner for his help and support during the preparation of this book.

The publishers would like to thank the Mansell Collection; Netherne Psychiatric Hospital Community Care; Sally and Richard Greenhill; and the Aldus Archive/Courtauld Institute Galleries for permission to reproduce the illustrative material in this book. Cover photograph courtesy of Sally and Richard Greenhill.

INTRODUCTION

Writing a book on *Living With Schizophrenia* is not easy. Most people with an illness accept that they have it and so are ready to receive advice as to how to cope, even though they may not always take that advice – as can be seen in the continued consumption of cigarettes by those with heart and lung disease, the diabetics who regularly tuck into forbidden foods, or those with high blood pressure who neglect to take their tablets because they do not feel ill. Unfortunately, at certain stages in a schizophrenic illness there is a loss of insight, so that the patient cannot fully accept that there is anything wrong with them. I believe, however, that even then there is a part of them which realises that things are not as they should be and that this accounts for the bewilderment, depression and fear that they frequently experience. This loss of insight, of course, is one of the reasons why relatives find it so hard to cope.

One would not expect anyone who is in the acute stages of schizophrenia to benefit from this book because, by its very nature, their illness will preoccupy them, to the exclusion of anything else. Similarly, one would not think that a person who is in an intensive care unit with a severe heart attack would feel inclined to read a book entitled, for example, *Living With Your Heart Problem* at that particular time. However, I hope that this book will help schizophrenics to understand their illness better as they respond to treatment and will assist them in making both the right decision about their lives and about the management of their condition. Moreover, I trust that the relatives, who frequently bear such a big burden in care, will find it helpful.

Few conditions can have been as misunderstood as schizo-

1

phrenia. It is a tragic illness, because it affects young people at a time when their abilities and prospects should be at their prime. But added to this is the attitude of society in general. We have mercifully left behind the days when a psychiatric illness was a reason for locking a person away, but public understanding of a condition like schizophrenia still has a long way to go. It is appalling to me to hear people, otherwise intelligent and humane, talk about 'nutters', 'the funny farm' and 'loony bin', and to regard schizophrenia as a subject for sick jokes.

This attitude, of course, is produced by a mixture of fear and ignorance. Because someone with schizophrenia does not always behave in the expected way, others do not know how to react. This embarrassment is not uniquely applied to those with a psychiatric illness; it is noted by those who have been bereaved, people who have suffered disfigurement and even victims of cancer. Ignorance leads to the idea that someone with schizophrenia may become unpredictable and violent. It is true that such patients sometimes behave in strange ways and say odd things, but this, surely, is not a reason for being fearful of them. Our society would be rather richer if we were more tolerant of harmless individuals whose only fault is that they do not always conform to our norms of social acceptability. The idea that schizophrenics are prone to commit horrendous acts of violence can certainly be discounted. Most such crimes are committed by individuals who pass in the community as normal, whatever that term may mean; just because we often cannot understand their motivation is no reason for thinking that they must be schizophrenic. As I hope this book will make clear, schizophrenia is an illness with a definite set of symptoms: it is not a label to be pinned on to anyone whose dark deeds we cannot understand. The majority of individuals who have a schizophrenic breakdown are law-abiding and extremely tolerant, considering the way they are frequently treated by society.

Because the cause of the condition is still unclear, it is natural that many theories have been put forward as an explanation. There are those who regard schizophrenia as being a product of environmental pressures or even a myth, designed to enable society to cope with its more recalcitrant members. I do not think that anyone who has worked with many schizophrenic patients would accept either of these conclusions. They are not borne out by the fact that the illness is common in all cultures and, as far as can be ascertained, at all times of history. Moreover, such beliefs, which seem to be held by those who feel it is more 'respectable' to be a victim of society rather than of a biochemical disorder, are completely nihilistic as regards the possibility of treatment. Naturally, stress must play a part in producing the condition, as it does in most illnesses, but all the evidence is that there is more to the etiology than that. If indeed the biochemical theories are to a certain extent pointing in the right direction, a cure may well be within our grasp.

However, the fact that, in the view of most psychiatrists, schizophrenia is an illness and not a label pinned by society on to those of its members who do not conform does not relieve society of its responsibility for tolerance and support. The old fashioned treatments often made the patient worse and further isolated them. Moreover, the presence of a few strange ideas does not make someone a subject for corrective treatment.

What I have endeavoured to demonstrate in this book is that schizophrenia is an illness, or a group of illnesses, with understandable symptoms which are frequently distressing but which can respond to treatment. The idea that those individuals who develop it are the subjects of special mystical visitations or recipients of some eternal truths, denied to the rest of humanity, is one bandied about by people who have never seen the reality of the illness in its more harrowing aspects. Their efforts to understand the world of the schizophrenic may be commendable, but having schizophrenia is rarely a life-enhancing experience and I think it is more beneficial to regard the condition as a disabling one for which, hopefully, a cure will soon emerge.

My aim is to give an understandable explanation of this complicated condition, not only for the patients and those close to them, but for any lay person who encounters it, in the hope that it will enable them to view someone with a schizophrenic illness with greater tolerance and sympathy.

1

A BRIEF HISTORY

The term schizophrenia, meaning literally split mind, was first used by the German psychiatrist Eugen Bleuler in 1911 to denote what he regarded as the fundamental disturbance in this mental disorder, namely a splitting or loosening of the association of ideas, so that thinking becomes severely disordered and a splitting between thinking and emotion leads to inappropriate behaviour.

EARLY DAYS

The symptoms which are now grouped together under the term schizophrenia have been known from the earliest times, and a large proportion of those regarded as insane and needing confinement in the past were probably schizophrenic. Although in some countries such individuals, with their odd behaviour and strange ideas, have been regarded as possessed of special mystical powers, in most instances schizophrenics have been the object of severe and thoughtless cruelty. They were burnt as witches or left to wander round the countryside as destitute beggars. Later, in the old asylums like Bedlam, they were chained, treated like animals, degraded in every way and often regarded as a peep show for a fashionable outing.

A more humane era began in 1795 when Pinel, inspired by the early ideas of the French Revolution, opened the door of *La Salpétrière* asylum in Paris, believing that strict confinement must inevitably make a mentally disturbed patient worse. He found there patients who were so forgotten that no one could remember them being admitted, many who had rarely seen daylight for years, and some who had constantly had chains around the whole of their body simply because their frantic struggles were misinterpreted as evidence of violence. He discovered that some had even lost all symptoms of their illness, and most were able to benefit enormously from proper care and normal surroundings.

It goes without saying that the majority of those appointed to care for the mentally ill, including their doctors, had become insensitive and indifferent to the patients' problems. The illness of George III, who suffered not from schizophrenia but from periodic episodes of madness probably due to a metabolic disorder called porphyria, was characterised by his confinement under conditions of great cruelty, which paid scant attention to any consideration that he was the monarch.

THE 19TH CENTURY

The 19th-century psychiatrists, certain of whom did so much to bring enlightenment to a particularly dark area of medicine, made a great study of schizophrenia and gave many descriptions of the condition in their writings. One of these pioneers, John Connolly, in his book *An Enquiry Concerning the Indications of Insanity* (1830) describes, amongst others, the case of Mr Matthews (p. 41):

> who, it seems, considered himself to be the especial object of annoyance from a mysterious gang, residing in some unknown apartment in London Wall, who, by their skill in pneumatic chemistry, were enabled to inflict on him various kinds of torture, of which kinds of torture and of the persons inflicting it, he would give a very minute account. Sometimes they constricted the fibres of his tongue, sometimes they spread a veil beneath his brain and intercepted communications between the mind and the heart; they would afflict him with stone in his bladder; introduce ideas at will to float and undulate in his mind; compress him almost to death by magnetic atmosphere, excoriate his stomach, force fluids into his head, lengthen his brain and produce distortion of all images and thoughts; and now and then they distended his nerves with gas.

One could not have a better description of typical paranoid

schizophrenia. Connolly wrote his book in an endeavour to prevent widespread abuses, whereby harmless patients who had persecutory delusions, but who in personality were mild and inoffensive, were committed to lunatic asylums.

However, it is interesting to reflect that the earlier part of the 19th century was, in many ways, a more enlightened era than the one that was to follow. Partly because of the pressure of industrialisation, and in association with Victorian paternalism, there developed the idea of incarcerating the mentally ill patient in large institutions, situated well away from the towns and far away from their relatives. These institutions can still be seen today, for example in the ring of psychiatric hospitals around the outskirts of London.

This action, of course, had its humane side, in that it was felt that a disordered mind would benefit from 'asylum', that is, being removed from everyday stresses to a life in tranquil surroundings. In practice, however, it led to many schizophrenics losing contact with their families and often with reality itself. Many of them, once committed, remained in hospital until the day they died, even if they had recovered from their illness. A committed 'lunatic' lost most of his or her civil rights.

Bethlem Hospital.

There was no effective treatment for the illness, and all but the most devoted relatives grew tired of waiting and lost interest in the patient. Spouses divorced them and their children grew up knowing nothing about them. One of the great tragedies of the illness was the way in which it alienated the sufferers from those who loved them, because often they appeared unable to respond emotionally or intellectually. Moreover, public lack of understanding was such that to be mentally ill was to be rejected by society.

THIS CENTURY

The advent of psychoanalysis added nothing to the treatment of schizophrenia, since Freud did not consider that it would be responsive to his methods. But the analysts brought a new attitude towards mental illness in general, by demonstrating that psychological factors could give rise to physical symptoms such as paralysis, blindness and loss of memory. They also showed that these problems could be alleviated by psychotherapeutic means if the underlying stresses were treated, thus removing the idea that the mind and body were independent entities. Gradually it became apparent that a psychiatric illness could happen to anyone.

But although a number of psychiatric conditions became increasingly explicable, schizophrenia still remained a mystery. Moreover, despite the fact that about a quarter of schizophrenics recovered spontaneously in the days before any effective treatment, it still had the reputation of being a frightening and incurable illness. The methods of treatment that were used – locked wards, segregation of the sexes, ineffective but unpleasant medication and, possibly most important of all, social isolation – tended to worsen rather than improve the illness. Many patients lost contact with the normal tasks of everyday life such as shopping, managing money, cooking, travelling in public transport and so on. They were dressed in clothes provided by the hospital rather than chosen by themselves, and so much like a uniform that they could easily be distinguished when they made excursions into the outside world.

Real improvement only began in the 1950s with the advent of new methods of treatment, the re-emergence of the earlier ideas of allowing patients freedom and self respect and the opinion that long-stay patients should spend their time doing useful and fulfilling work instead of sitting around in over-crowded, poorly decorated and uninspiring wards. Along with this came a new idea of the dignity of the schizophrenic patient and the view that they should have the same rights as other people who are ill.

Community care

Many schizophrenics are now able to return home to their families, since their period of hospitalisation is much shorter than in the past and there is considerable community support. A number, however, have to rely upon their own resources, and it is their care that must give rise to considerable concern. There is a very obvious need for more community facilities. There is no point in closing the large mental hospitals so that patients, who were at least comfortable and not completely lonely there, find themselves in worse conditions. The mentally ill deserve something better than to be wandering the streets as destitute beggars and sleeping rough or, even worse, to find themselves sent to prison for offences arising from their illness, merely because there is no room for them in the psychiatric units. More than any other group, they need not only lodgings but an understanding environment which will help them to cope with the inroads of their illness. The mental hospitals can only be closed when it is possible to provide proper community care for all those who need it.

2

WHAT IS SCHIZOPHRENIA?

Schizophrenia is a major mental illness which affects the entire personality. The degree to which it does so appears to depend upon the age at which the illness commences. Schizophrenia can be likened to a condition such as diabetes in which there are widely ranging degrees of severity, but in which all symptoms can be controlled by treatment. Thus a severe diabetic will need to take insulin injections or tablets, whilst a less severe one, who develops the illness later in life, possibly in relation to being overweight, may find all the symptoms relieved when he or she diets to a normal weight and pursues a restricted carbohydrate regime. In the same way, some people with schizophrenia need to take constant medication to control their symptoms, others need medication for a much more limited period, whilst a number, in whom an acute stress such as physical illness or childbirth has precipitated the illness, may have a complete recovery from symptoms in a relatively short space of time.

NEUROSES AND PSYCHOSES

It is customary to divide psychiatric illness into two main groups:

- Neuroses
- Psychoses

Neuroses

In a **neurotic** condition there is an exaggeration of normal patterns of behaviour, to the extent that they become

PSYCHIATRIC DISORDERS (see glossary for definition of terms in *italic*)

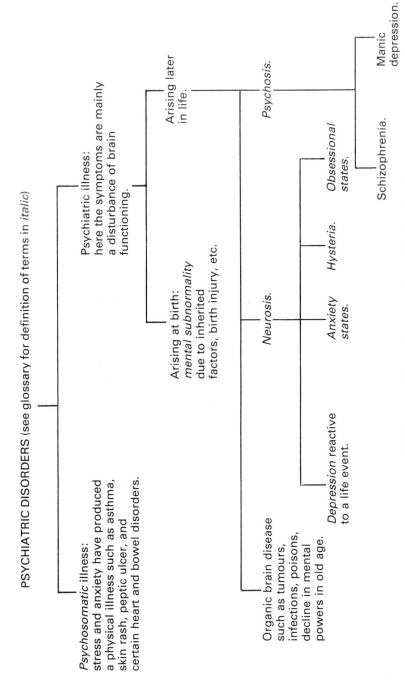

Psychosomatic illness: stress and anxiety have produced a physical illness such as asthma, skin rash, peptic ulcer, and certain heart and bowel disorders.

Psychiatric illness: here the symptoms are mainly a disturbance of brain functioning.

Arising at birth: *mental subnormality* due to inherited factors, birth injury, etc.

Arising later in life.

Organic brain disease such as tumours, infections, poisons, decline in mental powers in old age.

Neurosis.

Psychosis.

Depression reactive to a life event.

Anxiety states.

Hysteria.

Obsessional states.

Schizophrenia.

Manic depression.

The relationship between the main types of psychiatric disorders.

incapacitating. For example, anxiety in response to stress is a healthy and sometimes life-saving reaction, but when it not only continues but becomes progressively more severe after the cessation of stress, it becomes abnormal. The anxiety may be generalised, so that the sufferer feels constantly fearful, although he or she does not understand why, or it may become localised to a particular object or situation so that a phobia of heights, closed spaces, animals and so on develops. Similarly, the normal desire to be fairly orderly and have things in their place, or to be concerned about questions of right or wrong, can become magnified into a state of obsession, where an excessive concern over cleanliness or constant rumination over some trivial misdemeanour comes to occupy an individual's whole life.

The sufferers from neurotic illness realise that their symptoms are abnormal, although this does not necessarily help to alleviate them. Their personality and intellectual capacity are preserved and, although often severely incapacitated, they can lead normal lives to a greater or lesser extent.

Psychoses

Psychotic illness, on the other hand, involves the whole personality of the patient, causing them to lose insight so that they cannot accept that they are in any way ill. The illness leads to changes in emotion and thinking and to abnormal ideas, which often give rise to problems for them in the community. Whilst most people can imagine themselves becoming a victim of neurotic illness under certain circumstances, it is much harder for them to emphathise with psychotic illness, so that psychotics frequently find themselves alienated from those around them.

The two main groups of psychotic illness are:

- **manic-depressive psychosis**; and
- **schizophrenia**.

In manic-depressive psychosis there are periodic swings between excessive elation and overactivity – mania – and profound depression. In mania, individuals can become extremely excited and irritable, and develop unrealistic grandiose ideas of their position in society, their wealth and their general capabilities. This leads them into great difficulties in society. For example, a patient of mine, who lived on sickness benefit, somehow contrived to have five Rolls Royce cars delivered to his door, to the great consternation of his wife.

The converse of this manic mood is a profound depression when the patient believes him or herself to be guilty of some diabolical crime for which they will be eternally punished. They cannot eat or sleep and are frequently preoccupied with suicidal thoughts. They feel so guilty that they must confess to any crime that is publicised. At one murder investigation, where two young children were found murdered adjacent to the grounds of a psychiatric hospital, detectives were overwhelmed by 'confessions' from depressed elderly patients.

HOW MANY PEOPLE SUFFER FROM SCHIZOPHRENIA

The incidence (or rate at which new cases occur) of schizophrenia in the general population is about 1 per cent, that is one person in every 100 members of the population, so it is clearly not a rare disorder. The scale of the problem can be seen when it is realised that there are nearly a quarter of a million schizophrenic patients in the United Kingdom at any one time – as many as those who suffer from rheumatoid arthritis and 20 times more than those with multiple sclerosis. It is not in itself a fatal disease, but one which causes untold unhappiness for sufferers and their families.

It occurs in all types of societies, including primitive communities, although the incidence in the latter is hard to calculate because many schizophrenics are never brought to medical attention, their abnormality often passing unnoticed where the intellectual demands of society are not great. There is little difference overall between the number of men and women who develop schizophrenia. It can begin at any age from early teens to late life, but is more common in late adolescence or early adulthood. The age of commencement tends to affect the type of symptoms that predominate and, also, the inroads that the illness makes upon the personality.

HOW DOES SCHIZOPHRENIA MANIFEST ITSELF?

Part of the problem in discussing the symptoms of schizophrenia is that, since there is no known cause of this illness at present, symptoms and causation cannot be reliably related. It may be that the condition is a cluster of illnesses rather than a disease entity as such. Moreover, there can be a wide variation of symptoms depending upon age, personality and problems of each individual patient. Schizophrenia may begin quite suddenly, usually in response to some stressful event, or develop slowly over a period of weeks or months before being recognised. However, whatever the mode of onset, schizophrenia is an illness which causes disorders of thought processes and content of thinking, strange feelings leading to emotional disturbances, disordered perceptions of the external world and withdrawal from its realities.

The symptoms can be grouped as follows:

- Disorders of thinking
- Disturbances of feeling
- Delusions
- Hallucinations
- Disturbances of movement

Disorders of thinking

There is difficulty in thinking in schizophrenia, so that the thought processes become illogical, consecutive ideas being linked only tenuously to each other. This leads to the schizophrenic's conversation going round and round the point, so that one can realise that he or she is trying to answer a question but cannot get the thoughts marshalled correctly. For example, when asked where he or she has been a patient may answer 'Out and about, in and out, round in circles. It's all related. It's this theory of relativity that makes people leave a different trail.' It is obvious that an attempt is being made to answer the question, but that the mind is being influenced by many extraneous ideas which the patient cannot sort out. In other words, the normal way in which the brain selects certain ideas and pieces them together to provide coherent information is profoundly affected in schizophrenia. The patient has obviously understood the question and has indeed answered it to a certain extent. However, his attention has then become focused on the word 'related', which leads on to a similar sounding word 'relativity', which he begins to incorporate into a persecutory idea of 'people leaving a different trail'.

This inability to answer to the point can be demonstrated by asking a schizophrenic to explain a proverb with which normally he would have no difficulty. Asked for an explanation of 'Too many cooks spoil the broth', for example, one may get replies such as 'It's all to do with the kitchen', 'There are too many people there', 'Interference ruins a good dinner'. When thinking normally, such patients would have been quite able to give a general meaning, such as that excessive interference from too many people can lead to any scheme or action being ruined. A sign of improvement is when the thoughts can be marshalled more effectively.

In all schizophrenics there is some difficulty with thinking, and in severe cases the patient may be completely mute, utter only isolated words or, in answer to any question, reply monotonously with a single, apparently inappropriate word. Sometimes a new word – a **neologism** – which can appear quite inventive, may be used, such as 'blanketyboo' for feeling sad or 'growlinger' for feeling angry. One of the first symptoms in an adolescent may be an increasing and incapacitating difficulty in self-expression, so that a previously intelligent youngster turns out an examination paper which is completely nonsensical. In other cases there is a sensation that thoughts are racing wildly through the head and cannot be controlled, or, conversely, that thought has ceased altogether.

It is quite common for a schizophrenic to imagine that his mind and thought are under the control of an external agency, a symptom called **feelings of passivity**. There is a belief that the thoughts can be read by other people, that alien ideas are being implanted in the mind or that all thoughts are being drained out of the brain. It is of interest that these ideas have moved with the times and that many schizophrenics are very up to date with events. A hijack, a murder or the aberrant behaviour of some prominent personality rapidly becomes the focus of schizophrenic thinking, so that they believe themselves to be taking part in these activities. One patient recently told me that he had had an 'emulator' implanted in his brain by the Ministry of Defence, so that they could broadcast all his thoughts on to a screen to ensure that he did not betray them. Television is now regarded by schizophrenics as the typical way in which their thoughts are being broadcast and their misdemeanours advertised to the whole world. The fact that television person-alities are imagined to be indicating to the world at large intimate details of the schizophrenic's personal life probably accounts for the high mortality rate of television sets in psychiatric units.

There may also be a preoccupation with vague mystical and philosophical ideas which are meditated on in a completely unproductive way. Questions such as 'What is God' and 'What is the meaning of the universe' preoccupy the patient's mind, to the exclusion of everything else and without any kind of conclusion being reached. Sometimes these preoccupations are of a depressive nature, so that for example the ticking of a clock measures the minutes of the individual's remaining life. Pages may be covered by meaningless, repetitive writing which is felt to be a great and profound piece of work.

There is often, also, a preoccupation with minutiae. In fact it appears that one of the difficulties in schizophrenia is that of not being able to see things as a whole. Thus, in painting a picture, a schizophrenic may draw in only one corner of the paper or, when asked to interpret a design, seize on one small aspect to the exclusion of everything else.

The poverty of thinking, which the patient can recognise, may lead to the giving of laconic answers such as 'perhaps', 'may be', 'possibly', 'I don't know', which appear to an outsider to indicate a lack of cooperation, but which, in reality, illustrate the profound difficulties with the thought processes.

Disturbances of feeling

Schizophrenia may herald its onset by a mood change, either of depression or more rarely of elation. Sometimes, there may be states of ecstasy in which the individual is silently rapt in contemplation. Almost always there is blunting of emotional reaction to many life situations, so that important happenings are treated with apparent indifference, a symptom which relatives find particularly distressing. There may be emotional incongruity when the patient will burst into uncontrolled laughter on reception of bad news, relate gruesome delusional experiences with a broad smile or sob bitterly at a pleasant event. They may be wrapped up in their world, unable to communicate with those around, and relatives will often experience a 'pane of glass' sensation which well describes the feeling that they cannot get through to the person who is ill.

17

Delusions

These are false beliefs which cannot be altered by an appeal to the patient's reason and, very importantly, are alien to their cultural and intellectual background. Thus it is not particularly abnormal for a primitive tribesman to believe in voodoo and witchcraft. It becomes rather more bizarre when such a belief is tenaciously held in the suburbs of Woking or Cheltenham.

In schizophrenics these delusions stem from a primary delusion, which is a sudden and, to the patient, completely convincing belief that some everyday event has a profound and special significance. The form that this belief takes depends upon the previous personality of the patient. Thus, an intensely religious girl may suddenly decide that the way in which a fellow traveller in a train folds his newspaper indicates that she has been chosen to fulfil a special and important purpose, such as giving birth to a new Christ. A suspicious man may feel, from the way in which cars are parked outside the house, that he is being continually watched by agents desirous of obtaining information which he possesses. On the basis of a primary delusion it is relatively easy to understand how life events and the sceptical attitude of others leads to secondary delusional interpretation, the patient feeling that he or she is the innocent victim of widespread persecution.

Delusions may take various forms.

- **Paranoid** delusions are those of persecution, where there is a belief that the individual is being watched and singled out for some harmful end.
- In **grandiose** delusions there is a belief that the patient is some special individual, often with great powers.
- In **depressive** delusions the patient believes him or herself to be guilty of some terrible crime or to be responsible for horrific world events.

Such delusions can lead to all types of bizarre behaviour. A patient who believes he is on secret service duty may be up all night wandering round the countryside looking for hidden weapon dumps, undercover agents or special messages; not surprisingly, he comes home in a dishevelled state and sleeps all day. Someone convinced of a calling to a Messianic mission insists upon stopping passersby in the street to convert them and upbraiding, often at risk of personal danger, those who offend against his principles.

The idea of delusional beliefs has been the subject of much controversy amongst non-medical commentators. Mystics are frequently quoted in this connection, since they often feel that they have some special powers and communion with God. The distinction is that many of them have acted in conformity with their beliefs, whereas the schizophrenics show inappropriate behaviour. Thus, a lady who believes she is the Queen of England, and possessed of incredible wealth, will be quite content to remain in hospital refusing to buy any new clothes. I looked after two patients who were the best of friends, slept in adjacent beds on the ward and went everywhere together. One was a fanatical communist who believed the whole ward was involved in a Catholic conspiracy. The other, an ardent Catholic, had an equally intense belief that he was the victim of international communism.

In any case, the presence of delusions in themselves is not an indication for treatment, despite the pressure that is sometimes applied in the community. It depends very much how far they interfere with a person's life or the lives of those around them or how unhappy it makes them. Thus, one would be very concerned if a schizophrenic mother thought her normal child was grossly abnormal and that it would be a kindness to take its life; it would be apparent that she was not only out of touch with the reality, but, because of this, in danger of committing an action which she would bitterly regret when she was well, and which was out of context with her normal character. A person who feels constantly persecuted and followed everywhere by agents who plot to kill him may well become seriously suicidal. On the other hand, delusional ideas can be quite harmless and even a source of comfort. For many years, I looked after, in the community, an elderly lady who believed that she was constantly having babies. Her consumption of blue and pink knitting wool was enormous, but she was rewarded by her 'children' in the form of dolls and teddy bears, all with names, arranged on her sofa. In such cases it can be the relatives or neighbours who cannot accept the situation.

It should be emphasised, moreover, that, despite the intense conviction and often unpleasant nature of delusional beliefs, very few schizophrenics show serious tendencies to violent and antisocial behaviour.

Hallucinations

These are false perceptions of sensations which are not present in reality in the external world. This distinguishes them from illusions, where there is a misinterpretation of a real object so that, for example, a piece of paper blown along by the wind may appear to be a small creature such as a mouse or rat.

Hallucinations may occur in association with any of the senses, but characteristically in schizophrenia they are mainly **auditory**, taking the form of 'voices' which mock the patient, or are abusive, or amusing, making the schizophrenic laugh by some witticism. Sometimes the voice takes the form of a familiar person, but often patients will have difficulty even in differentiating the sex. There may be the feeling that voices are emanating from animals; possibly some of the unfortunate witches who were burnt may have experienced auditory hallucinations from their 'familiar', a black cat. Others believe that voices come from the television, criticising their every move, exposing their innermost thoughts or commenting on their life. Patients will often shout at their 'voices' or giggle at the funny remarks they can hear. They often are extremely reticent about what the 'voices' say, however, and are usually much less forthcoming about them than they are about their delusions.

Visual hallucinations are much less common in schizophrenia. Visions of whole scenes, for example, are more characteristic of psychosis induced by drugs such as cannabis. Sometimes, however, schizophrenics do see people or things that are not there. A patient of mine thought that she had a ghost of her dead brother-in-law sitting in a particular chair in her living room. Unfortunately, he resisted all attempts to remove him, changing seats whenever a chair he favoured was taken away.

Tactile hallucinations can give rise to the belief that the patient is being interfered with sexually, or electricity is being put through them by their persecutors. A very respectable middle-aged lady, a pillar of the local community, caused consternation when she shouted at the bewildered vicar in the middle of his service that he should cease his 'phantom sexual attentions' to her immediately, whilst an adolescent confounded the headmaster of her private school by announcing at assembly that he was the father of her unborn child conceived entirely by telepathy.

Hallucinations of **taste** and **smell** can also occur, so that what appears to be the peculiar taste of food causes a paranoid individual to believe he or she is being poisoned. Severe and dangerous refusal of food may develop which, in the absence of treatment, can be life-threatening. One married couple who shared a delusion about poisoning solved this problem quite neatly, however; the dominant wife instructed the passive husband to taste all the food first and only ate when he appeared to be unaffected.

Bearing in mind the persuasive nature of these hallucinations, it is not surprising that they cause agitation, hostility and sometimes aggression. Patients are often distressed to hear the voices of their loved ones apparently plotting their destruction. Sometimes the voices give dangerous instructions to the sufferer about ending their life. Always they are completely compelling to the patient, who accepts them implicitly.

Disturbances of movement

Depending on the condition, there may be gross overactivity and excitement, so that the patient is ceaselessly moving about in an aimless yet frenetic way. At the other extreme there can be severe retardation, so that the schizophrenic sits in a chair all day or retires to bed, refusing to get up.

A similar pattern is seen in the disorders of volition, which can lead to the patient being lethargic and unable to be motivated to perform everyday tasks such as getting up in the morning to go to work. A schizophrenic mother may neglect her child, not out of any intent, but because she lacks the will to get up to feed or care for it. One of the major problems of rehabilitating those with long-standing schizophrenic illness into the community is the effort required to motivate them to look after themselves adequately and to maintain anything like a normal work schedule. Understandably, these symptoms are a source of irritation and distress to the relatives, but it must be emphasised that this lack of initiative is due to the illness and not to laziness or lack of effort on the patient's part.

WAYS IN WHICH SCHIZOPHRENIA CAN DEVELOP

The most common time for schizophrenia to arise is in the middle or late teens and the onset is frequently insidious and

21

initially difficult to distinguish from normal behaviour. Adolescents in our society are characteristically moody, at times overly preoccupied with their appearance and at others grimy and untidy; they tend to experience violent fluctuations of mood, to swing alternately between rebellion and overdependence and to spend long periods alone in their rooms. In addition, things are now complicated by the possibility of the intake of illegal drugs which, indeed, may be associated with schizophrenia. A number of schizophrenics may take stimulant drugs in an effort to make them feel less depressed or to improve their energy.

A schizophrenic illness may herald its approach in a teenager by a persistent change in their behaviour. Thus a previously diligent scholar begins to get poor school reports, fails examinations and so on; an amiable child becomes unpredictable, aggressive and temperamental. Often there is inability to sleep at night and the individual remains in bed half the day. More significantly, however, there is the onset of disordered thinking and inappropriate reactions, often with evidence of delusions and hallucinations. The teenager loses interest in everything, becomes withdrawn, hostile and can be seen responding to 'voices' by smiling or shouting. Often there may be depression and a suicide attempt. Sometimes there is excessive concern with appearance, so that the young person spends hours in front of the mirror looking at a small pimple or going to the doctors asking that a quite normal nose should be altered. Persistence of such behaviour is always suspicious, and where a parent cannot understand the reasons for their child's behaviour, it is time to seek expert help. Unfortunately, the fear of the illness and the lack of insight and cooperation on the part of the patient, often intensified by adolescent cussedness, combine to make diagnosis and treatment difficult. All too often the doctor is presented to the patient as some kind of 'corrective agent' to induce better behaviour, the adolescent is not made aware even that he is being visited and the parents are at loss to know how to cope; the patient is frightened, and therefore hostile, and time needs to be taken to build up a relationship before a diagnosis can be established.

Schizophrenia can also manifest itself in a much more acute form in teenagers and, more notably, in the 20–40 age group. Such episodes are associated with stress of all kinds – a broken marriage, problems at work, bereavement, childbirth and so on. The patient, previously normal, becomes quite abruptly very disturbed. There are delusions, hallucinations, changes in emotion and thinking so that there appears to be a complete personality change. A woman suddenly accuses her husband of being unfaithful, locks him in the bathroom so that he cannot go to work and, if he manages to get away, follows him in her dressing gown, bursting into his place of work to find evidence of his misbehaviour. She becomes unable to look after the home, the children and herself. Or a man suddenly decides that he is a new Christ, starts giving away all his money, refuses to sleep, and goes around without eating or taking care of himself, preaching what, in reality, is complete nonsense to astonished bystanders. This is naturally a most distressing experience for those around, but they can be reassured that in a majority of cases there will be a complete recovery. Indeed, the more acute the disturbance, the more complete the recovery to normal life.

In general the later in life the onset of schizophrenia the more preserved the personality remains; this is seen characteristically in the form of late onset of schizophrenia called **paraphrenia**. Here there are delusions of persecution with hallucinations, but with good preservation of the intellect and personality. The illness may begin for the first time in the 60s or 70s and is especially common in single or widowed elderly women. The patient develops the idea that he or she is being persecuted and, in females, the delusions frequently take the form of sexual interference. There is often a history of solitariness and loneliness, and defects of vision and, especially, hearing problems are common. The patient becomes increasingly preoccupied with her persecutions and importunes the police or her supposed persecutors with complaints or abusive letters. There is no evidence of loss of memory or intellectual capacity and these conditions respond well to treatment with neuroleptic drugs (the major tranquillisers).

Potentially, normal intelligence and knowledge are preserved and many schizophrenics reveal in their conversation and writing that they still retain their mental abilities. In recovery from an acute schizophrenic episode, intellectual ability will usually be unimpaired. However, patients with a long-standing schizophrenic illness cannot make adequate use of their intelligence because of thought disturbances, lack of volition and drive, and preoccupation with delusional and hallucinatory ideas.

THE OUTLOOK IN SCHIZOPHRENIA

About a quarter of those who develop a schizophrenic illness make a complete recovery. This is particularly so in cases where the onset of the illness is very rapid and the symptoms very acute. Interestingly, a similar proportion of schizophrenic patients recovered in the days when there was no treatment, provided infection or other illness consequent upon their agitated condition did not supervene. Connolly's records, in particular, show a number of cases of obvious schizophrenic illness occurring after childbirth where the patient was able to return home after about a year. In these acute cases it appears that spontaneous recovery took place within about 10–12 months, and this period has now been considerably shortened by the use of psychotropic drugs (drugs that act on the mind).

It is in the remaining group of schizophrenics, previously regarded as almost untreatable, that modern therapies have made such a difference. These patients have varying degrees of thought disorder, emotional problems and disturbances of volition. They frequently retain delusions which interfere with their functioning in society and, in particular, lack the drive and initiative to look after themselves adequately, to maintain a family, find a job, or cope with demands of everyday life. With treatment, a high proportion will have their symptoms relieved, avoid relapses and lead a reasonable life in the community. In a minority, drug treatment is less satisfactory and these are the patients who may need to remain in the hospital environment.

The factors which affect the outcome in schizophrenia have been extensively investigated and it would seem that the following are important.

- The **age of onset**. In general, the earlier the illness starts, the more destruction there is bound to be of the developing personality.
- The **mode of onset**. As noted previously, an acute illness often leads to a more complete recovery. A slow insidious onset often results in persistence of symptoms.

- The retention of **good emotional responses**. In general, those patients who are still able to relate to others in a warm and meaningful way appear to be able to cope better, possibly for a variety of reasons not least of which is that they can still make good relationships.
- The presence of a **precipitating stress**. Those patients who develop a schizophrenic illness after childbirth, for example, usually make a complete recovery.
- The nature of **support in the community**. It is perhaps not surprising, in view of the nature of schizophrenic illness, that the quality of the environment is very important. Those patients who are discharged to lodgings and hostels where things are impersonal do not do well. Neither do patients discharged to parents and spouses if there is high 'expressed emotion', that is, the relatives make critical comments, are hostile and over-involved, demanding more from the patient than he or she can fulfill. The patients who do best are those who go to live with more emotionally neutral friends, tolerant relatives or in small well-supervised hostels. This should not be seen as a criticism of relatives or spouses, who are usually only too anxious to do their best but who are often, understandably, at a loss as to how to cope, and who are bound to be emotionally involved with the patient.
- The willingness of the patient to **comply with the treatment**. Treatment will be discussed at length in Chapter 6, but there is little doubt that relapse of schizophrenic symptoms can often be directly related to the decision of the patient to refuse to continue with their prescribed medication.

HOW CAN SCHIZOPHRENIA BE CLASSIFIED?

It must be said at once that no classification can be wholly satisfactory, since it cannot be based upon an adequate theory of causation. However, classification does mean something. First of all, many sufferers and their relatives will hear a 'label' applied to the illness, which it is as well for them to understand. Secondly, classification is an aid, not only to possible outcome and treatment now but also in helping to pinpoint a constellation of symptoms which may assist in future research into the complex causation of this condition.

Earlier classification

Earlier classification divided the illness into four categories.

- **Simple** schizophrenia, where the onset is in the early teens with the predominant feature being the fragmentation of the personality. Such patients tend to show a loss of initiative, emotional flattening and withdrawal from life rather than many delusions or hallucinations.
- **Hebephrenic** schizophrenia, which occurs later in the teens or early 20s, with a predominance of thought disorder.

Both simple and hebephrenic conditions tend to progress to a more long-standing chronic schizophrenic state.

- **Catatonic** schizophrenia, where the onset tends to be at a later age, in the middle to late 20s. The predominant symptoms are acute states of excitement or depressive withdrawal, accompanied by delusions and hallucinations of a transient nature. The illness develops suddenly and has a very good response to treatment, usually with a complete recovery.
- **Paranoid** schizophrenia. In this condition the predominant feature is the fixed delusions of persecution, accompanied by auditory hallucinations. There is relatively good preservation of personality and the condition responds well to psychotropic drugs.

A newer classification

But many symptoms overlap and now psychiatrists tend to use a new classification.

- **Type I** schizophrenia, where there are many positive symptoms.
- **Type II** schizophrenia, in which negative symptoms predominate.

This distinction is important with regard to outlook and treatment. Positive symptoms can be seen as those which cause the patient actively to do things, such as delusions, hallucinations, mood changes of excitement or depression and acute thought disorder. They respond rapidly to treatment.

Negative symptoms are those that come on insidiously and are characterised by what the patient fails to do, e.g. lack of volition, emotional flattening, withdrawal from society so that there is inability to communicate or socialise. Here the response to treatment is not so dramatic.

3

WHAT CAUSES SCHIZOPHRENIA?

The answer is that, unfortunately, at the present time nobody knows and this is why there have been so many theories. The causation of any illness is never simple. Even an infection such as measles or tonsillitis, which seems a straightforward reaction to a viral or bacterial attack, also depends upon other factors such as previous exposure, level of immunity and degree of resistance. More complicated conditions obviously have a wider variety of causative factors. Consider a common problem such as coronary thrombosis (heart attack); although we know a great deal about the possible risk factors such as raised blood pressure, increased serum cholesterol, smoking, obesity and family history, it is still impossible to know what makes one individual have a heart attack whilst another with the same risk factors does not. It is unclear, for example, how far stress plays a part in this and in many other illnesses. The heart is a relatively simple organ compared to the brain; consequently the understanding of why and how mental illness occurs must be exceedingly difficult. Schizophrenia is not alone in being an illness which is imperfectly understood, so it is all the more encouraging to see how far our knowledge about its causation has progressed in the last couple of decades.

In recent years there has been a considerable amount of research in the fields of genetics, biochemistry, psychology and epidemiology, all of which has led to a number of interesting results. Like those of a jigsaw puzzle, these pieces still have to be fitted together accurately and there are doubtless some bits missing, but it is possible that in the foreseeable future a theory can be formulated to explain why certain individuals develop a schizophrenic illness. I think it would be fair to say that at the present time the main weight of psychiatric opinion regards the causation as multifactoral, holding the view that the illness may be provoked by the effects of environmental disturbance, psychological stress or physical illness in an individual predisposed to develop schizophrenia by genetically based factors.

Possible causative factors can thus be considered under the following headings.

- Genetic
- Biochemical and organic factors in the brain
- Psychological
- Environmental

GENETIC OR INHERITED FACTORS

As compared to the average incidence of about 1 per cent for schizophrenia in the general population, there is a significantly raised rate for those who are close relatives of someone with a schizophrenic illness. The risk of developing schizophrenia is about 12 per cent for those who have a brother or sister with the illness – that is, they have 12 times more chance of becoming schizophrenic than someone with no family history of the disease. A similar figure, of about 16 per cent, applies to a child with one schizophrenic parent and it rises to 40 per cent if both parents are schizophrenic.

One of the important ways of estimating the degree of genetic involvement in a particular disease is by comparative studies of identical and non-identical twins. Identical (or monozygotic) twins are formed by the splitting of the same fertilised egg at conception; they are therefore genetically identical. Non-identical (or dizygotic) twins are produced when two separate eggs are fertilised by separate sperm; they are thus no more genetically identical than their other brothers or sisters. Figures show that a monozygotic twin has a 50 per cent chance of developing schizophrenic illness if the other twin already has it, whereas for dizygotic twins the figure is about 14 per cent, similar to that for siblings in general. Significantly, this rate of 50 per cent does not fall when monozygotic twins are reared apart. And schizophrenia also occurs at the expected rate in children of schizophrenic parents who are adopted at an early age into non-schizophrenic families. Both these facts indicate that environment and upbringing alone cannot be the key to schizophrenia and that an inherited element must play a part.

However, one should not overestimate the genetic factor. Schizophrenia is not a hereditary illness in the sense that it is passed from one generation to another quite clearly, as is the case with haemophilia or Huntington's chorea (a degenerative brain disorder). It would be more accurate to describe it as familial – that is, tending to occur more in some families than in others. Nor does it have such a high risk rate as a condition like diabetes, where there is a family history in at least 50 per cent of cases. The increased rates of schizophrenia within some families do not conform to either a dominant or recessive mode of inheritance – patterns that would tend to indicate that the disease was controlled by a single gene (unit of inherited material). The most likely explanation is that, in those prone to developing a schizophrenic illness, there are a number of genes controlling various traits, and certain environmental factors can trigger these genes into action, resulting in subsequent illness. This allies it very much to the surmised causation of high blood pressure, where there are similar findings for incidence within families and where an underlying failure in the workings of the body's biochemistry is postulated. Genetic research, which has played such an important role in a variety of illnesses where inherited factors are involved, may well eventually provide considerable clues in both these disorders.

Different types of schizophrenia may be related to differing types of genetic makeup. About one-third of schizophrenic patients have a history of a shy, withdrawn and socially isolated personality which dates back to early childhood. Their illness tends to develop gradually, as distinct from the acute illnesses in those of an active, outgoing personality. Personality itself is governed to a large extent by inherited factors and this so called 'schizoid' personality may be rendered more vulnerable to external stress by his or her genetic endowment. It should be emphasised also, to bring this discussion into perspective, that many schizophrenic patients do not have a family history of the illness at all. This again indicates the possibility of not one but a number of genetic factors being involved, which come together by chance.

BIOCHEMICAL FACTORS

It has been postulated that the inherited tendency may take the form of a biochemical abnormality in the brain which is, as yet, imperfectly understood. Many early psychiatrists drew attention to the thin build and poor peripheral blood circulation common in the schizophrenic, factors which led to the suspicion that it was a metabolic disorder. In recent years a number of such disorders, often based upon an inherited failure to make use of certain essential chemicals in the body, have been shown to cause severe mental problems. One of the earlier ones to be demonstrated was phenylketonuria, a rare condition where there is a failure of those enzymes which break down a substance called phenylalanine in the brain. This leads to severe mental deficiency if the diagnosis is not established immediately after birth by the simple method of testing the blood of the newborn babies for abnormal phenyl-ketones (the Guthrie test) and, if this is positive, applying an appropriate dietary regime.

The idea that the origins of schizophrenic illness may lie in a biochemical disturbance has been strengthened by some recent developments. It has been shown that several of the so-called hallucinogenic drugs, such as mescaline and LSD, can produce a similar picture to schizophrenia, although the hallucinations induced by these drugs are mainly visual and not auditory. Other drugs used therapeutically, notably the steroids like cortisone, which have a wide-ranging effect on body metabolism, may produce a similar paranoid illness. Moreover, large doses of amphetamines – stimulant drugs such as dexedrine or benzedrine – can provoke a psychotic illness which is similar to schizophrenia in that there are paranoid delusions, hallucinations and mood changes. Amphetamines are known to release a substance called dopamine in the brain, so increasing its concentration. Dopamine is a neurotransmitter or a chemical which carries messages from cell to cell within the brain. The neuroleptic drugs (major tranquillisers), which are used to treat schizophrenia, all have in common their power to act as antagonists of dopamine receptors within the brain, so that dopamine concentration is reduced. And one of their side-effects, the production of Parkinson's disease, is itself connected with decreased dopamine activity.

Because of all these factors, it has been suggested that in schizophrenia there is overactivity of central nervous system pathways in the brain involving dopamine and that this overactivity is in some way related to the symptoms of the illness. It has been postulated that a genetically based inability to deal with dopamine or one of its precursors may be triggered off by environmental events, which is why the condition does not manifest itself until adolescence or early adult life. By specialised X-ray techniques it can be demonstrated that a number of schizophrenics do have increased concentration of dopamine in their brains, but there is still a considerable way to go before we have substantial proof of this interesting hyopothesis. Indeed, the dopamine disturbance may only be part of a more widespread cerebral dysfunction.

ORGANIC FACTORS IN THE BRAIN

It has long been known that conditions where there are areas of damage in the brain, such as head injuries, brain tumours or temporal lobe epilepsy, can cause psychotic symptoms similar to schizophrenia. In recent years computerised tomography (CT) scanning has been developed to visualise the brain and its various areas. This is a form of specialised X-ray, where two-dimensional pictures of the head can be processed by a computer to give images of all brain areas in great detail. This technique has been used in the early stages of schizophrenia and it has shown that, in many schizophrenics, the ventricles or channels and spaces within the brain, through which the cerebrospinal fluid flows, are enlarged. This means that, since the brain is encased in a rigid box, the skull, there must be some small loss of brain tissue. Such enlargement of the ventricles is present from the earliest stage of the illness and is not progressive.

This finding has led to increased interest in possible early brain damage as a cause of schizophrenia. A factor which may be connected with this is the observation that schizophrenic patients in northern countries are born significantly more often in the cold winter months. It has been suggested that some environmental factor associated with winter birth, such as a virus or complications in pregnancy or labour, could lead to such early cerebral damage. The increased ventricular size

31

shown on the CT scan is more common in those schizophrenics with a history of obstetric complications at their birth. Some workers have postulated that this damage does not become apparent until the brain matures sufficiently to call into operation the more complex levels of functioning. This would account for the peak incidence of schizophrenia being in adolescence and early adult life. The other possibility is that the genes which regulate the development of the central nervous system (the brain and spinal cord) may be at fault in some way. This must obviously be only in a minor way, since general cerebral development is not affected – there is usually no evidence of delayed intellectual development in those who later show symptoms of schizophrenia.

There is also evidence to suggest that in schizophrenic patients there is an imbalance of dominance between the two halves (hemispheres) of the brain; usually the left half is dominant, making the majority of people right handed. In the dominant hemisphere are located the centres for speech, thoughts, emotions and their consequent actions. It is thought that where there is confusion about which hemisphere is dominant, the brain may misinterpret stimuli which are produced and perceive them as auditory hallucinations, thought disorder and delusions.

PSYCHOLOGICAL FACTORS

The failure to find a treatable physical explanation for schizophrenic symptoms has led to increased interest in psychological interpretations of the condition.

Some researchers have regarded schizophrenia as a way of behaving in response to the conflicting messages of irrational and intolerable emotional relationships. Thus, the illness is seen as originating from the development of distorted interpersonal relationships within the family. It is considered that these have to be changed by a psychotherapeutic approach if the patient is to recover. He or she is regarded as being a 'scapegoat', who has to bear the responsibility for the problems and distress of the family; for example, a couple with marital problems may blame all their troubles on their son, who takes refuge in a schizophrenic illness. It has been suggested that undue dominance by one parent, the so-called 'marital skew', or the 'double-bind' phenomena, where one thing is said and another meant, can cause schizophrenia. The concept of the so-called 'schizophrenic mother', who alternates between displaying apparently irrational feelings of love and rejection, has also been introduced. It has been suggested that such mothers themselves have schizophrenic traits so that they may be passing a schizophrenic gene to their child, and there is an assumption that the mother has a predominant role in this. However, this is not supported by the fact that when a child of a schizophrenic parent develops this illness the affected parent is just as likely to be the father as the mother.

No one can doubt that some of these studies have contributed to our understanding of family dynamics, but none have been able to show that schizophrenic families are different from other families in the community. Many schizophrenics do not have more than the usual degree of differences with their family, and only a very small minority of them have been subjected to greater emotional stress than the average child during their childhood. Moreover, when assessing the role of relatives, one has to take into account their considerable distress at having a sick member, particularly in the case of parents. Nor can family disagreements, no matter how serious, fully account for the severity and prolonged nature of a number of schizophrenic breakdowns.

Some attempts to explore the world of the schizophrenic have concluded that they have opted out from a harsh and irrational world into a state where, in some way, they have a better vision of life. This view, in my opinion, cannot be substantiated. The vision of the world as depicted by an artist like Van Gogh or a poet like John Clare was certainly different when they were ill with their schizophrenic symptoms. However, they were both bitterly unhappy at this time. Most schizophrenics are equally bewildered and frightened by their illness, not comforted by it.

ENVIRONMENTAL FACTORS

Schizophrenia occurs in all countries, both developed and underdeveloped, although, naturally, its incidence in the latter is much less easy to assess because in third world countries a number of schizophrenics never receive treatment. As far as is known, the incidence is not increased noticeably by conditions of national stress such as wars, catastrophes such as earthquakes and floods, and imprisonment in concentration camps.

This does not mean to say, however, that stress may not trigger off a schizophrenic illness in a predisposed person. Studies have shown that many schizophrenics experience a high frequency of stressful events in the three weeks prior to the onset of their illness. Such events included matrimonial problems, loss of a job, death of a close relative, financial problems, or serious illness or injury. The importance of stress as a precipitant, however, does not seem as great as in other psychiatric disorders such as anxiety or depression and, as in all such studies, one has to disentangle whether the stress provoked the illness or vice versa.

The characteristic of most stress-related illnesses is that they improve when the stress is removed, whereas most schizophrenic illnesses do not. Someone with a depression related to environmental problems may well become much better when admitted to hospital for a short time and then become worse when they go home, even for a weekend. This rarely happens in a schizophrenic condition, as could be observed in the days before any effective treatment existed and when hospital conditions were such as to deter anyone from wishing to remain there willingly.

In addition, most reactions to stress are designed to escape from it in some way, whereas many schizophrenics seem to find themselves imprisoned in an even more stressful situation by the nature of their illness. Their behaviour often induces punitive rather than sympathetic treatment; concentration camp survivors, for example, will tell of the obviously catatonic schizophrenic who stood by the barbed wire, ignoring the commands to move by the guard, and was shot.

It is claimed that stressful events may precipitate a relapse in a schizophrenic illness. Much attention has been directed to the role of expressed emotion (EE), which is measured by an assessment of the degree of criticism, hostility and over-involvement on the part of the family to the patient. High EE in those living with their families was correlated significantly with a high probability of relapse. This is not remarkable, though; few normal individuals, who have a much greater opportunity to escape from the environment, would care to tolerate such an atmosphere for long. Moreover, one has to take into account the effect that the patient's behaviour may have on the family, with an emotional vicious circle being produced. Maintenance anti-psychotic drug therapy appears to be protective against such relapses, but cannot completely prevent them.

Physical stress may also be involved in some cases of schizophrenia, particularly infections and childbirth, although depression is more common. The disability produced by defects of vision and hearing can play a part, particularly in the paranoid illnesses of later life.

The general consensus appears at present to be that stress may play some part at the onset of a schizophrenic psychosis, but it is not the most significant factor. Stress may exacerbate relapse in an established illness, which is quite explicable in view of the many difficulties that such patients have.

Schizophrenia does tend to be associated with poor social conditions – a great proportion of schizophrenics are found living in decaying urban areas and belong to the lowest social class 5, because they are unemployed or in unskilled manual work. The evidence, though, is that they have drifted into this state because of the inroads of their illness. Schizophrenics also have a low marriage rate, especially as far as the males are concerned, and a high divorce rate, but this again is quite explicable since the onset of the illness in early adult life must militate against the formation of long-lasting close relationships and the responsibilities of marriage.

CAN SCHIZOPHRENIA BE PREVENTED?

There is no evidence at the present time that most preventive measures can stop anyone developing schizophrenia, but this does not mean that some practical measures cannot be taken. Obviously, where there is a family history of the illness in a close relative and one finds an adolescent who has a shy, withdrawn, introverted personality, there is the possibility of the condition developing. The warning signs will be discussed in the chapter on living with schizophrenia (Chapter 9). It is wise in these circumstances for the relative to encourage outgoing activities and friendships as much as possible, although without pushing the young person unduly. Excessive demands for socialisation can be just as damaging to a vulnerable personality as isolation. Moreover it can be just as counterproductive to be constantly looking for symptoms of illness when it does not exist. Many people prefer their own company, enjoy solitary activities and feel little need for the companionship of others, without being in the least danger of developing schizophrenia.

It is important, however, that parents do not desert an adolescent who does appear vulnerable. They may often feel that the young person is self-sufficient and that, because he or she does not communicate very well, parental support is not needed. This is far from the truth. The early history of many of those developing a schizophrenic illness at the beginning of adult life shows an increasing social isolation, which may be associated with the onset of the illness but which may also contribute to producing it.

Childbirth

There is also no way in which the occurrence of schizophrenia after illness or childbirth can be predicted. A schizophrenic illness may appear for the first time after the delivery of the second or third child, for example. In those who develop such an illness for the first time in the couple of months after the birth, it is usually the case that the baby is wanted and the marital relationship good. There may, however, be a history of physical stress such as prolonged labour or severe haemorrhage after delivery, and it is possibly the exhaustion rather than the actual stress of childbirth that produces the illness. A schizophrenic illness occurring in the subsequent postnatal period is usually very acute, but responds well to treatment, with complete recovery. It is also, fortunately, rare, postnatal depression being much commoner.

Drug abuse

There is one factor, however, that is very relevant to the development of schizophrenia, and that is drug abuse. It has been known for some time that the amphetamine group of drugs, traded as blues, speed, dexedrine and so on, can give rise to a psychosis very similar to schizophrenia. The individual may become suspicious, begin to hear voices and develop a series of persecutory delusions. Other drugs such as LSD, cannabis, marihuana, may also precipitate a similar condition.

There has been debate as to whether the drug-taking is

initiated by someone who is already having schizophrenic symptoms, in an attempt to make them feel more active. But there is no doubt that, in certain individuals, even small doses of these hallucinogenic drugs can be extremely dangerous. The psychotic condition produced does not always clear up readily and may lead to a prolonged schizophrenic illness. With LSD in particular a single dose can lead to fatality; the drug may provoke a suicidal depression, or disturbances of perception can lead, for example, to the user falling from a high building in the belief that he or she is only walking down a small step. In addition, these drugs can certainly cause a relapse of an established illness. Therefore, it is vital that young people should avoid these drugs and that parents, and the community in general, should reinforce this avoidance.

4

RECOGNISING SCHIZOPHRENIA

The diagnosis of schizophrenia is a serious one, but, as I hope I have made clear, it is an illness which can be treated. It also is important to remember that in a quarter of cases complete recovery occurs. Because early diagnosis and treatment can substantially assist in minimising the inroads of the illness, it is important to be aware of the warning signs of the condition.

RISK FACTORS

So what kind of factors may put people at risk?

- **Age**. The illness most commonly begins between the ages of 18 and 25.
- **Personality**. The so-called 'schizoid' personality is regarded as being a predisposing factor in a number of people. From childhood the personality has been shy, introverted and solitary. Such individuals have difficulty in forming relationships with either sex as they enter adolescence and have problems in establishing emotional contact with others. Perhaps because of this, they prefer work and hobbies where they have to mix with as few people as possible. However, many people with this personality never develop any type of schizophrenic illness, and many individuals who do become ill are outgoing and extroverted, so other factors must play a part.
- A history of taking hallucinogenic **drugs** such as LSD or amphetamines.
- A severe **infection** or an **operation** which may act as a precipitant. Symptoms usually begin within a few days.

- Recent **childbirth**, particularly where labour has been prolonged, where there has been severe haemorrhage or there has been concern because the baby is physically frail.
- The taking of certain drugs, particularly the **cortisone** derivatives, for therapeutic purposes.
- **Defect of vision or hearing**. In particular cases a middle-aged or elderly person may be at risk. They are usually single, female, living alone and suffering from some defect of vision or hearing which interferes with their accurate perception of their environment.
- **Family history**. A history of schizophrenia in a close relative such as a parent or sibling and, especially, in an identical twin.
- **Stress**. Severe stress at work or at home under any of these circumstances.

EARLY SIGNS OF SCHIZOPHRENIA

And what are the early signs?

Gradual withdrawal from society and friends
A young person begins to spend increasing longer periods in his or her room. This, of course, is not uncommon in adolescence but, in the case of a developing schizophrenic illness, it is accompanied by complete inactivity. The individual is quite content to lie most of the day in bed doing nothing. This daytime lethargy may often be combined with overactivity at night.

An older person may decline to open the door to relatives or friends because they are frightened that someone will harm them. This may go on to become a problem with food and drink, which they imagine could be poisoned by their persecutors.

Decline in performance
Someone who is developing schizophrenia will find it hard to concentrate. This will obviously be more apparent in a person in an intellectual occupation. For example, it becomes hard for them to do serious studies and prepare for examinations; a formerly promising pupil finds him or herself getting poor marks, being unable to understand things as quickly as before

and failing their exams. Someone in a more manual occupation cannot get up in the morning in order to be at work on time, and there are complaints about their slowness and poor work performance.

Excessive preoccupation with physical appearance

Most adolescents are very much involved with how they look. They worry considerably about being overweight, having acne, being attractive to the opposite sex and so on. An exaggeration of this may be one of the early symptoms of schizophrenia. The adolescent stands for hours in front of the mirror constantly examining a minute pimple, ruminates endlessly about the shape of their nose or the fact that their hairline seems to be receding.

Depression

Sadness and feeling low in spirits are common symptoms of psychiatric problems in every age group. Schizophrenia is no exception, the depression often seeming to be a part of the illness rather than related to real life stresses. It may show as tiredness, loss of interest in everything, a feeling that life is not worth living, or poor appetite and sleep.

It must be emphasised, however, that depression as an illness in itself is much more common than a schizophrenic illness, so it is not necessary to assume that every depressed adolescent must be developing schizophrenia.

Changes in activity

The onset of schizophrenia may be heralded by a decline in activity, so that the individual becomes lethargic, always appears tired and remains most of the day in bed.

On the other hand, particularly where there has been an intake of drugs or a physical problem, there may be a purposeless overactivity. The person becomes restless, leaves their home to wander round the streets, arriving back unkempt and exhausted. During this time their behaviour may lead to them being picked up by the police or becoming involved in quarrels with strangers due to their interfering behaviour. One of the first signs of a schizophrenic illness may be a sudden disappearance from home for no apparent reason.

Strange ideas and behaviour

Since, by definition, a delusion is maintained without any insight into its bizarre nature, it is impossible for the patient to recognise that they are suffering from them. Delusions are frequently kept secret, but may emerge in the form of bizarre accusations of those around. Thus a husband may be convinced that his wife is being unfaithful to him, may return from work to spy on the house or hide in a wardrobe in the bedroom to spring out on an imaginary lover. All his wife's protestations fail to convince him and his belief becomes more and more firmly held. Or a girl may refuse to go to work because she is convinced that all her workmates are plotting against her, are saying that she is a prostitute, laughing at her all the time and even plotting to kill her.

Naturally there is a fine line between these fears and normal feelings of rejection, suspicion or betrayal, but delusional beliefs are characterised by their increasingly fantastic nature. You may believe that you are unpopular at work, but this rarely, if ever, extends to the belief that your workmates are plotting to do you serious physical harm.

Such delusional beliefs may be revealed only by strange behaviour. There may be a refusal to eat any food in case it is poisoned; rooms are explored for bugging devices and hidden traps; the movement of cars in the street is watched for hidden persecutors; numerous letters are penned to prominent people, containing nonsensical complaints.

Disturbances of thinking

Since disturbances of thinking are common in schizophrenia, those around may notice that it is difficult to understand completely what someone who is developing the illness is saying. The conversation is often full of allusions to philosophical and mystical topics which, when examined, make no sense at all. This will become particularly apparent in someone who has previously had an intelligent grasp of subjects and who could speak succinctly and to the point.

The patient may feel that their mind is in a muddle and complain about it in a puzzled way.

Emotional changes

One of the most hurtful aspects of this illness for the relatives can be the way in which the patient, be it a child or a spouse, suddenly becomes quite emotionally withdrawn. The patient may realise this and complain that they cannot feel as they used to do. This is particularly marked in relation to children or to a husband or wife, where the expression of warm feelings is natural.

At other times there seems to be a difficulty in expressing the appropriate emotion. A person when told of a bereavement may speak about it quite indifferently, only to weep copiously some time later when a subject of no importance is being discussed. This does not mean that real grief is not felt, only that it cannot be expressed.

Hallucinations

These are usually in the form of 'voices' which plague the patient. They are rarely admitted to, but are often frightening. They may be of a derogatory nature, laughing and sneering. The individual feels compelled to answer and, since there is no awareness that the voices are not real, may be deeply distressed at hearing a previously trusted and loved person apparently saying mocking and hurtful things. Naturally, this leads to a feeling of mistrust and increased withdrawal. At other times the voices may be amusing, causing the patient to laugh at him or herself.

Feeling that everything has special significance

There may be the feeling that people on television are broadcasting personal details, again referring to things in a derogatory way. Or an individual may become angry because of the way the table has been set or the car parked, feeling that these have a special and mysterious meaning. Such a small incident may trigger off an outburst of temper and reproach.

Physical illness

Schizophrenia is a distressing and disturbing illness. The sufferer often becomes hypochondriacal, feeling that the mental changes must be associated with some serious illness. They may frequently attend the doctor for vague and changing complaints. Their apathy may also extend to a loss of interest in eating, with a resulting loss of weight. Alternatively, ceaseless activity may cause them to look exhausted and contribute to the weight loss. They may seek refuge in smoking countless cigarettes or over-indulging in alcohol.

THE DIAGNOSIS

The diagnosis of schizophrenia is one that must be made by a professional. Many of the symptoms described may be due to other conditions which will require entirely different types of treatment; sometimes, for example, they are associated with the normal problems of adolescence which will be alleviated in time.

It may also take a period of observation to see whether the illness will develop into schizophrenia. However, the earlier advice is sought, the more quickly something can be done to help.

5

PLANNING THE TREATMENT OF SCHIZOPHRENIA

Before the advent of the psychotropic drugs, a large percentage of patients with schizophrenia could expect to be in hospital two years or longer and many were never sufficiently in control of their symptoms to leave hospital to live in the outside world. Nowadays a considerable proportion of patients can be treated as outpatients or day-patients from the start, without the necessity for hospitalisation and separation from their family and their environment. There are still a number of sufferers who will require the support and the long-term treatment that a hospital-type environment can provide. (What this treatment should be will be discussed in the next chapter.)

The way in which schizophrenia should be treated can be divided into several phases according to the nature and degree of the illness. It should always be based upon the following.

- The initial assessment of the patient and of the severity of the illness.
- Talking to the patient and the family, explaining the illness and the proposed treatments.
- A discussion as to whether treatment should be as an inpatient, day-patient or as an outpatient.
- Treatment of the symptoms of the illness by means of the appropriate medication.
- A long-term plan to help the individual continue to function in the community as a family member, at work and in his or her previous environment.

SEEKING HELP

It is unfortunate but true that schizophrenia remains a frightening illness, both for those who develop it and for people in the community. This is partly because the symptoms themselves can be alarming but also because the illness carries quite unfounded ideas about violent behaviour. The theme of certain Hollywood films, for example, is that a seemingly normal person can commit horrendous crimes under the influence of a 'split personality', which is considered to be synonymous with schizophrenia. This has nothing to do with the reality of a schizophrenic illness, as a survey of the symptoms will make clear. Schizophrenia is a serious illness, but one that can be treated. Crimes of violence are no more common amongst schizophrenics than in the general population and one is certainly far safer walking through a psychiatric hospital than walking through the streets of a big city.

But this public image dies hard. It is not only a cause for rejection by those who know little of the illness, but also a reason why many sufferers and their relatives do not come forward earlier to seek advice and help. Psychiatrists share in this rejection, to the extent that some people express shame at having to see one. It cannot be stressed too often that a nervous problem is, essentially, no different from a physical one. Indeed, there is considerable evidence that psychiatric problems may often have their roots in a disturbance of bodily function, in the same way as a physical illness. Conversely, it is now known that factors such as stress, depression and anxiety may play a part in precipitating or increasing the gravity of physical illness. The time when the mind and the body were seen as separate entities is long past.

Unfortunately, since there is often a loss of insight at the start of schizophrenic illness, it may well be the relatives who have to seek help first. However, when trust is built up, many individuals who feel their symptoms returning are not afraid to seek advice and talk about their problems. This trust with the doctor, community nurse, social worker or counsellor is one of the most vital factors in treating this illness, so that the isolation and loneliness often experienced can be alleviated and prompt help obtained if the problems recur. This is vital in preventing the disruption of family and community life that recurrent admissions to hospital can involve.

ASSESSMENT

The usual way in which someone with a possible schizophrenic illness may be seen is at an outpatient clinic, on a home visit or, sometimes, at a health centre. It is becoming more frequent for psychiatric services to be based in the community. Psychiatric outpatients are conducted in a general hospital in the same way as other clinics, and patients are referred there by the family doctor. However, your doctor may feel that the problem is so urgent that it may be more helpful for the psychiatrist to make a home visit. This will enable the specialist to see what the home conditions are like, to talk to your family and to decide what would be the best way to help you.

Schizophrenia is an illness which can present in a number of ways.

Problems that are not schizophrenia

Firstly, there are those who are not schizophrenic at all, but where it is feared that they might be.

Jean was a 16-year-old shy girl who found it difficult to make friends. She preferred to spend time alone in her home reading, in order to avoid what she saw as inevitable rejection by her peers. Her parents had an unhappy marriage and her mother had always made it clear to Jean how unpleasant she found any sexual relationships. Therefore Jean avoided boys, dressed frumpishly and was teased by the girls at school because she was not 'with it'. Many of the big talkers amongst her classmates boasted of their sexual experiences and Jean finally made a suicide attempt, telling her doctor who treated her that it was because she was 'the only virgin in the school'.

Her parents had difficulty accepting that their child's condition had anything to do with their attitudes. They had recently read an article about schizophrenia and felt sure that their daughter was suffering from it. However, Jean had none of the classical symptoms, and her problem needed counselling and environmental management.

Paula was a disturbed adolescent, with a history of self mutilation, who was found wandering on the motorway by the police. She refused to give her name or address or say anything about herself. Her arms were covered with cuts and she was unkempt and unwashed. Observation in hospital, however, revealed that her behaviour was quite purposeful and there was no evidence of the unpredictability or response to delusions and hallucinations that one might find in schizophrenia. It emerged that she had run away from home because of repeated sexual abuse and violence.

John, aged 28, had always worried about his health. Every time he read a medical article – and he was always fascinated by accounts of disease – he concluded that he was suffering from the condition described. Having exhausted the possibility of physical problems, he turned to the psychiatric field. He became obsessed with the idea that he might be developing schizophrenia, after seeing an old Hollywood film. He was more than eager to see a psychiatrist, with whom he spent a considerable time discussing his fears that he might 'break out' and do some drastic deed. In reality, treatment had to be directed towards helping him to discover the reasons why he needed to feel that he was ill.

Delusions can occur in a number of psychiatric conditions and have to be seen in the context of the other symptoms.

George, aged 21, had failed his university exams and faced an uncertain future. In addition, his girlfriend had left him for another man. He became progressively more depressed, lost weight and could not sleep. He began voicing ideas that he was a wicked person, that people were following him to kill him because he was not fit to live and that his life was not worth living anyway. However his illness was typical of depression and he responded well to antidepressants and counselling.

Not every seemingly strange idea is a delusion.

Maria, aged 71, was firmly convinced that her relatives were taking her pension and stealing small sums of money from her home. She lived alone and was rather socially isolated, so she complained to her doctor. He was persuaded by her plausible nephew that Maria was suffering from delusions and the psychiatrist was called. Maria greeted this doctor extremely pleasantly and gave a reasoned account of what had been happening. Further investigation revealed that, not only was the nephew systematically defrauding her, but that he also had a long history of petty theft.

Acute onset of schizophrenia

Secondly, there is true schizophrenia, which may present itself in a very acute way or more insidiously.

Acute schizophrenic illness is characterised by a very rapid onset, often in relation to stress, a physical illness, the breakdown of a marriage, childbirth, bereavement, work problems and so on. The response to treatment is just as rapid, but many acute illnesses require admission to hospital for a short period.

Emily, aged 22, came from the West Indies. She had only recently arrived in this country, and she knew few people. She was training to be a nurse in the casualty department of a London hospital, and one Saturday night there was a fracas in which some drunken youths were both threatening and offensive to her. Within the next few days Emily had become acutely paranoid. She refused to leave her room or to eat her food, maintaining that it was poisoned. She accused her fellow students of plotting against her and put a large notice on her door saying that, if she died, the police would know who was responsible. Attempts to dissuade her from these ideas met with resistance. She took to wandering around the hospital in her nightclothes, running out to the police station to ask for protection. She was eventually picked up in the street, where she was wandering in an attempt to escape her imaginary persecutors. She made a rapid response to treatment.

Irene, aged 24, was delivered of a healthy and much wanted baby. The delivery had been quite normal, but almost immediately afterwards she became withdrawn and tearful. This was attributed by her family and her doctor to postnatal 'blues'. However, Irene became increasingly unable to care for her baby. She voiced ideas that the child was not normal, that it did not really belong to her and that another baby had been substituted in the hospital. She then began to wonder if her baby was not an incarnation of some evil spirit. She refused to accept food for it prepared by the family, because she alleged that it was poisoned, and then refused her own food on the same grounds. Her thinking became disconnected and she upset her husband by calling him very formally 'Mr' and insisting that he was not her husband because she was really married to a well known pop singer. She was restless all night and her admission to hospital was finally precipitated when she wandered off with her baby in the pram, looking for her supposed husband.

She made a complete recovery within a few weeks. This was considerably assisted by the fact that she could be admitted with her baby to a mother and baby unit, so that her relationship with her child could be maintained.

Shaun, aged 25, had graduated in languages but, with a poor degree and a rather withdrawn personality, had some difficulty in finding a job commensurate with his qualifications. He finally became employed as a courier to a rather dubious travel company who specialised in the cheaper end of the holiday market. His first trip abroad saw him having to face many hazards – overbooking, unfinished hotels, irate clients, clients thrown into foreign jails for being drunk and disorderly and clients who ended up in hospital casualty departments with fractures after doing hazardous things such as dancing on the top of tables in nightclubs.

Poor Shaun, shy, reserved and non-aggressive, could not cope. He became very agitated, retired to his room and left all his party's return tickets in a pile in the front of the hotel foyer, saying the members of the group could either choose to travel on them or take the space shuttle to Mars which he was planning. He then appeared in the dining-room, where his unfortunate party were having their meagre meal, and pulled all the tablecloths off the tables, saying that they contained secret messages which he had to put together. He told the local doctor that he was employed by the space agency and his purpose abroad was to advise them on a new aircraft which would shortly depart into outer space.

It would seem very obvious that Shaun's delusions were based upon a desire to escape from his intolerable situation. His mother had had a schizophrenic breakdown some years previously. Shaun responded well to anti-psychotic medication, but required considerable help and support in adjusting to his work situation.

Jim, aged 30, worked in an office, but none of his fellow workers knew much about him because he never socialised. A conscientious worker, he was always punctual, but never discussed his personal affairs. He had never been absent from work previously, so his boss became alarmed when Jim did not appear for three or four days without explanation. Enquiry of his landlady established that she had not seen him for that time either. Jim was found in his room completely withdrawn.

When questioned, he laughed inappropriately, made facial grimaces and put his head under the bedclothes. He was dirty and neglected, had not eaten and refused to do so, spitting out any food that was offered.

He again made rapid response to treatment but during his recovery period showed many schizophrenic symptoms. It transpired that his mother, to whom he was devoted, had just died after a protracted illness.

Slow onset of schizophrenia

In many cases, however, the onset of a schizophrenic illness is more **insidious**, the illness coming on over a period of weeks or months.

Gary was 16. He began experimenting with cannabis at a party given by friends and his parents had noticed that he was increasingly withdrawn. His school work deteriorated and he began to wander round the streets instead of attending his classes. He was awake and wandering around the house at night and could only be roused in the morning with difficulty. When questioned, his replies were noncommittal, but it was noticed that he would laugh inappropriately and that he had begun to talk to himself. All his old emotional warmth had gone and he would do bizarre things such as tearing pages out of books and burning them, or cutting off bits of his hair. One day he shaved his head completely, telling his mother that he was covered with insects.

His parents at first attributed his condition to adolescent

behaviour difficulties, but his condition emerged as being the onset of a schizophrenic condition.

Paul was 19, a clever boy, who had just gone to university. There he was lonely and unhappy. He became more and more solitary and took to turning up at the police station, saying that the other students had told him to go there to be examined about a crime. There had been a number of rapes in the area and Paul kept confessing that he was the rapist. He told the police, by way of explanation, that an identikit picture they had broadcast on TV was just like him and that they themselves were naming him constantly over the radio. When questioned further, he launched into a confused harangue which puzzled everyone. He claimed to be a secret service agent and said that he had special information about the IRA which meant that they intended to kill him. He was a non-attender at lectures and, in the examination, returned a blank paper with a note to say that the questions all had hidden meanings and were intended to trap him. Medical advice was finally sought by his parents.

Gillian, aged 23, returned from a holiday abroad and announced to her parents that she was pregnant. Their initial distress turned to bewilderment when she announced that it was a spiritual pregnancy, produced by the seeds floating in the atmosphere. She refused to believe the gynecologist who told her that she was not pregnant, picked up a book from his desk and threatened to hit him over the head. She began a series of visits to the local hospital, complaining that the doctors had performed an abortion against her will by mystical means. She then started writing abusive letters to her medical advisers and complained to the authorities about the way she had been treated.

Her parents were reluctant to accept that she was ill, but were finally forced to seek medical help when their previously modest and retiring daughter began to accuse passersby of being part of the plot against her and to claim that her neighbours all had sexual designs on her.

Clare, aged 40, had always been a rather prickly and sensitive person. She had an argument with the next door neighbours about their unruly children. The neighbours were both unsympathetic and aggressive and made no attempt to curb their children's behaviour. Clare became increasingly paranoid. She claimed that the neighbours were sending noxious fumes through the walls of her house, that the children were pulling up all her plants in the night and putting down weedkiller and that the house was being bugged so that she was receiving constant electric shocks. She sent her husband out to buy various preparations to counteract these effects, boarded up all the windows, kept calling her doctor to examine her own children, whom she felt were dying from the poisonous gases, and finally became so fearful that she refused to allow any of the family to leave the house.

As is so often in these cases, her attitude to the neighbours led to increasing scorn and derision and Clare became so desperate that she spent a considerable time banging on the walls of the house, telling the neighbours what she thought about them. She herself eventually consulted the doctor about her tiredness and loss of weight, but the whole history soon emerged and it was obvious that she was suffering from a paranoid illness.

Jack, aged 50, was a tramp. He had been picked up by the police for loitering with intent; by this they meant that they had found him holding on to a door handle of a parked car and, when questioned, he had been unable to justify his actions.

He had spent most of his adult life wandering around the country, accompanied by an endearing mongrel dog who would perform tricks for anyone who happened to be interested. Jack slept mostly in Salvation Army hostels or in the open air. He had had schizophrenia for a number of years and, periodically, was admitted to hospital. He liked, as he put it, to 'winter' in a psychiatric hospital and relied upon finding a sympathetic doctor who would allow him to do so. Unfortunately, he had recently been viciously attacked by a group of louts who had also tried to hurt his dog. This had produced an exacerbation of his illness and his loitering was due to his preoccupation with his 'voices' and not to any sinister intent.

He improved considerably after a short period of treatment, but was soon out on the road again.

Kay was 45 and had had several schizophrenic breakdowns. In a supermarket one day she heard a voice tell her to take a portion of meat from the shelves. Helping herself, not to a fillet steak but to a piece of scrag end, she was apprehended by the store detective, taken to court and prosecuted by a zealous solicitor as if she were one of the great train robbers. Since she said not a word in her defence and sat with her back to the magistrates throughout the hearing, with cotton wool plugs in her ears and her beret pulled over her eyes, they very properly concluded that a psychiatric opinion might prove more beneficial than a custodial sentence.

Grace, aged 69, was a distressed gentlewoman. Unmarried, very ladylike and slightly deaf, she lived in a spotless house bequeathed to her by her parents. Unfortunately, Grace had developed the idea that people were coming into her house and stealing her property. She had a system of elaborate locks put everywhere, but claimed that she could hear the plotters laughing and saying that she could not fool them. She believed that they intended to drive her insane or to kill her, that they were digging secret passages under her house and putting listening devices all around the walls. She would spend hours looking for pieces of fluff or finger marks which she felt indicated their presence. In all other respects, though, she was quite in control of her affairs.

Thus it can be seen that a schizophrenic illness may come to attention in many ways and that the assessment must take into consideration all the factors that have precipitated it.

WHAT THE DOCTOR WILL WANT TO KNOW

- In order to make a correct diagnosis of the problem, the doctor will want you to talk about your symptoms, your feelings about them and whether you see them as a sign of illness. He or she is there to help you as an individual and to listen to you sympathetically.
- It will be helpful if a relative or friend can also give an account of how you appear to them. Often those close to you may be aware of a change that you have not noticed.

- Therapy aims at treating the whole person, so it is important that the doctor knows something about your earlier life, your personality, your attitudes, your hobbies, school and work life, your hopes and ambitions. It is important to build up a picture of how you see life so that the doctor can offer you the most constructive help.
- A physical examination is vital, so that any bodily illness which may cause nervous symptoms can be excluded.
- There are a number of drugs which may precipitate an illness with symptoms similar to that of schizophrenia. Some of them, such as amphetamines, LSD and cannabis, are taken illegally. Others, such as cortisone derivatives, are prescribed for medical conditions. It is important that the doctor knows exactly what medication you have taken recently.
- You may be asked what appear to be a number of pointless questions; for example, what a proverb means, or an elaboration on what you see in a drawing or painting. This is intended to give the doctor more insight into your thinking and emotions.
- Recent illnesses, upsets and difficulties are also very relevant to your present condition.

It may be objected that I have placed undue emphasis upon the role of the doctor and the medical model in general. I make no apology for this. The management of a schizophrenic breakdown involves team work, in which many disciplines participate. Some, such as the community psychiatric nurse, may play as important a part as the psychiatrist in this, if not more so. But it cannot be emphasised too strongly that a number of treatable, but potentially serious, physical illnesses may mimic some of the symptoms of a psychotic illness. Tragedies can occur when this fact is ignored. Therefore it is vital that diagnosis is made by someone who is medically qualified and who can exclude such conditions or observe that, concurrent with a schizophrenic illness, there is some other medical problem which requires treatment. A number of schizophrenics, for example, suffer from anaemia or vitamin deficiency due to poor nutrition; others are so self-obsessed that they neglect their physical state and ignore obvious illness.

6

TREATING SCHIZOPHRENIA

This can be considered under several headings.

- Treatment with neuroleptic drugs.
- Psychotherapy and counselling.
- Group therapy.
- Family therapy.
- Social therapies and behaviour modification.
- Diet.
- ECT.
- Alternative therapies.

TREATMENT WITH NEUROLEPTIC DRUGS

There is no doubt that the discovery of the neuroleptic drugs has revolutionised the treatment of schizophrenia, enabling the vast majority of patients to return to the community. It is all the more unfortunate, therefore, that they have been the subject of so much unjustified opposition. It is perfectly understandable that many schizophrenics object to the idea that they need medication, particularly when a number of them do not accept that they are ill. Moreover, resistance to the drugs is not confined to the schizophrenic patient, as studies of compliance with other medication, such as drugs given to reduce high blood pressure, will demonstrate. And how many people who have been given a course of antibiotics can honestly say that they have not forgotten to take them, or have stopped the course immediately they were feeling better?

However this is an entirely different matter to the ill-informed opinion which classes the psychotropic drugs as being on a par with substances such as Valium and Librium, both now known to be habit forming and of no long-term value in the management of nervous disorders. Tranquillisers such as Valium and Librium are very effective in controlling anxiety, which is why people can become dependent on them. However they do not necessarily help an anxious individual face up to those problems which perpetuate their anxiety, and it is this self-realisation which should be the object of therapy in neurotic conditions.

The psychotropic or neuroleptic drugs fall into a completely different category. They appear to control the symptoms of schizophrenia and to restore the individual to a normal mental balance. Given in appropriate dosage, they help rather than hinder a return to a full life. There is considerable evidence that they act upon substances in the brain which appear to be implicated in the causation of schizophrenia. It would be wonderful, of course, if a treatment could be produced which would cure schizophrenia in the same way as an antibiotic can cure an infection, but schizophrenia remains a complicated condition and these drugs are the best treatment we have at the present.

The psychotropic and neuroleptic drugs are so named because they have an effect upon brain functioning. There are various groups, but they all have in common the power to occupy dopamine receptors in the central nervous system. Dopamine is a neurotransmitter, a messenger, in nerve cells and its levels are reduced when the receptors are blocked by the neuroleptic drugs. The antipsychotic power of these drugs appears to be related to their ability to exert this dopamine receptor blocking. The theory underlying this is discussed more fully in Chapter 3 on causation (see pp. 27–37).

The main action of the neuroleptic drugs is on the positive symptoms of schizophrenia. They reduce or abolish the intensity of delusions and hallucinations, calm the excited agitated mood and lessen disturbed and aggressive behaviour. Most of them have less action upon withdrawal, apathy and the other negative symptoms, although it is claimed that some may have an activating effect.

What drugs are available?

The following drugs are used in the treatment of schizophrenia.

- **Clopixol** (zuclopenthixol)

  Tablets: given in doses of 20–30 mg per day, increasing to a maximum of 150 mg a day. The usual maintenance dose is 20–50 mg a day in divided doses.

  Injections: given by intramuscular injection as a long-acting depot preparation, 200–400 mg every 2–4 weeks. The active preparation is contained in thin vegetable oil as 200 mg in 1 ml of solution. It can also be given as a more concentrated injection every 1–4 weeks.

- **Depixol** (flupenthixol)

  Tablets: up to six tablets of 3 mg daily.

  Injections: again given by intramuscular injection as a long-acting depot preparation, processed in thin vegetable oil. A test dose of 20 mg is given, then 20–80 mg every two weeks. As a concentrate of 100 mg it can be given in doses of 100–200 mg every two weeks.

- **Dolmatil** (sulpiride)

  Tablets: 200 mg tablets taken twice a day up to a daily dose of 2,400 mg.

- **Droleptan** (droperidol)

  Tablets: used in cases of acute excitement, 5–20 mg every 4–8 hours.

  Injection: it can also be given by injection in cases of severe excitement.

- **Fentazin** (perphenazine)

  Tablets: 12 mg daily in divided doses.

  Injection: can also be used.

- **Haldol** (haloperidol)

  Tablets: (5 or 10 mg) or oral liquid (2 mg/ml or 10 mg/ml): taken as 0.5–5 mg two or three times daily, increasing gradually as required.

  Injection: given for acute excitement. As Haldol decanoate it can also be given intramuscularly as a long-acting depot injection of 50–300 mg every four weeks.

- **Integrin** (oxypertine)

  Tablets: 40 mg twice or three times daily, up to a maximum of 300 mg twice daily.

- **Largactil** (chlorpromazine) – the first anti-psychotic drug, discovered in 1952.

  Tablets: 25 mg three times a day, increasing to 300 mg a day.

  Can also be given as a syrup or an injection.

- **Melleril** (thioridazine)
  Tablets: 30–100 mg daily, increasing to 600 mg daily if necessary.
  It can also be given as a syrup.
- **Modecate** (fluphenazine decanoate)
  Injection: a long-acting injection of either 25 mg/ml or 100 mg/ml in an oily suspension. A test dose of 12.5 mg is given, then doses of 12.5–100 mg every 2–5 weeks.
- **Moditen** (fluphenazine enanthate)
  Injection: long-acting depot injection of an oily preparation. An initial test dose of 12.5 mg is followed by deep intramuscular injections of 12.5–100 mg every 2–3 weeks.
- **Neulactil** (pericyazine)
  Tablets: 15–75 mg daily.
  Can also be given as a syrup.
- **Orap** (pimozide)
  Tablets: 2–20 mg daily as a single dose. The usual dose is 4–10 mg a day.
- **Piportil** (pipothiazine palmitate)
  Injection: a long-acting depot preparation of 50 mg/ml in oily solution. A test dose of 25 mg is followed by 50–200 mg every four weeks, using deep intramuscular injection. The usual dose is 50–100 mg every four weeks.
- **Redeptin** (fluspirilene)
  Injection: 2–8 mg weekly, up to a maximum of 20 mg weekly.
- **Serenace** (haloperidol) – see Haldol.
- **Sparine** (promazine)
  Tablets: 100–200 mg four times daily.
  Injection: also used.
- **Stelazine** (trifluoperazine)
  Tablets: 5–15 mg daily, up to 30 mg daily.
  Can also be given as a syrup or an injection.
- **Veractil** (methotrimeprazine)
  Tablets: 25 mg tablets given at night as a sedative in excitement, dose increasing gradually as necessary.

What drugs should be used?
This depends upon the nature of the illness.

- In acute stages, where there is considerable excitement and restlessness, a short period of injections of chlorpromazine

(Largactil) or haloperidol (Haldol) may be necessary. In less severe states these drugs can be given as tablets or syrup.

- In patients where the main symptoms are withdrawal and apathy, more activating preparations such as Stelazine (trifluoperazine), Orap (pimozide) or Dolmatil (sulpiride) are beneficial.
- In those patients where paranoid delusions and hallucinations predominate, tablets or syrup of chlorpromazine (Largactil), haloperidol (Haldol) or Melleril (thioridazine) may be indicated.

Depot preparations

The depot preparations are used for the long-term maintenance of a schizophrenic illness. They are not necessary where an acute illness responds rapidly to treatment, but are invaluable where symptoms of illness persist. They have the benefit that they are not dependent upon the patient's remembering to take the tablets. They also exert a more stabilising effect upon the symptoms, and the evidence points to the fact that they prevent relapse. The type and dosage of the depot used will depend upon the individual patient, and there is often a particular drug which is more effective in the alleviation of individual symptoms. It is usual to give a small test dose of the drug before treatment is commenced to demonstrate any hypersensitivity.

In general, Modecate (fluphenazine decanoate), Haldol (haloperidol) and Clopixol (zuclopenthixol) tend to be used for more positive symptoms, whilst Depixol (flupenthixol) is claimed to alleviate negative symptoms. But there is a great deal of individual variation, and if one depot is not effective or gives rise to severe side-effects another can be tried.

Advice to patients on depot preparations

There are a number of factors to be borne in mind when a depot preparation is suggested to you as treatment.

- No one likes having injections, but these should be painless and will help you to overcome your illness.
- You will be given a test dose and will be asked to notice any side-effects. You may experience drowsiness, tremors or muscle stiffness. However, the vast majority experience no side-effects and tolerate the medication well.

- The full dose of the drug that you will be on will be given to you in about a week if you have no side-effects.
- You should be given a card which says exactly what medication you are receiving and the dosage. It should also tell you when you should come again for a further injection.
- The injection will normally be administered by a community nurse, but can be done by your family doctor or his clinic nurse.
- Many hospitals have a special clinic for administering these injections. However the injections should not interfere with your work or studies, and arrangements can often be made for them to be given in the evening. In other cases the psychiatric nurse will come to your home.
- You will have a contact telephone number of your community nurse. Report to her or your family doctor if you are unwell or experience any side-effects.
- Keep your appointments. It is important that the injections are given regularly, otherwise symptoms may recur.
- If you go on holiday or abroad for a period of time, arrangements can usually be made either to supply you with appropriate medication or to give you a letter to take to a doctor overseas. This should be discussed in advance with your psychiatrist, since not all medications are available in other countries and in some countries they are expensive.
- Having a neuroleptic drug does not normally interfere with you taking other medication or having inoculations against such diseases as typhoid and cholera. Discuss this with your doctor.
- Find a doctor and nurse you can trust and try to be honest with them about your symptoms. A change or alteration of medication may be indicated if you do not respond to one particular type of treatment.
- Never stop the injections abruptly. This could lead to a severe and disabling return of your symptoms.

Stopping the medication

It is wise to continue the medication until you have had no symptoms for at least a year. Then it may be possible to reduce the dose of the medication and to increase the time between injections, although this should be done over a six-month period. During this time you should be prepared to accept a return to your previous level of medication if your symptoms recur. Failure to do this could result in an increase in symptoms and serious interference with the life you have built up in the community.

Try to start reducing your medication when you feel settled in your family life and social situation. It is unwise to alter things when you are being subjected to stress, such as moving house or lodgings, a family bereavement, a change of job and so on. Bear in mind what feelings you could experience if your condition is relapsing and report to your adviser immediately you become aware of any of these feelings.

Don't try to rush things. It is better to reduce your medication gradually; in this way you have a better chance of staying well without it.

SIDE-EFFECTS OF DRUGS

Drowsiness can occur with large doses of the more sedative drugs such as Largactil and Melleril, while **faintness, dizziness** and **dryness of the mouth** may also be experienced.

Effects on the central nervous system

Excessive blocking of dopamine receptors in the brain (see page 58) by high doses of a neuroleptic drug or individual sensitivity to the drug (see below) can give rise to symptoms very like those of **Parkinsonism**, i.e. the symptoms of Parkinson's disease.
son's disease.

- There is a slowing up of the gait.
- Tremors of the hands occur, with the characteristic 'pill-rolling movement' where the thumb and forefinger are rubbed together as if a small object is being rolled between them.
- The face may lose its expression.
- Speech may be slow and slurred.

These side effects disappear with a reduction in the dosage of the neuroleptic drug and with the administration of an anti-Parkinsonian drug such as procyclidine (Kemadrin) or orphenadrine (Disipal).

Individual sensitivity may be manifested by acute muscular reactions.

- **Akathisia** – there may be a feeling of restlessness, so that the limbs constantly have to be moved.
- **Dystonia** – the muscles become fixed in abnormal attitudes so that the neck feels stiff or the jaw tight.

Both these conditions are fortunately rare. If they do occur they are alarming, naturally, but are promptly alleviated by the administration of anti-Parkinsonian drugs, either as tablets or, in severe cases, as an intramuscular injection.

Tardive dyskinisia is a condition which may occur after several years of treatment with high doses of neuroleptic drugs. It takes the form of involuntary repetitive movements of the limbs, trunk and face, being particularly noticeable in the muscles around the mouth. The development of this condition can be prevented by close monitoring of drug therapy and regular examinations. It is also lessened by giving as small a dose of the neuroleptic as is necessary to control the symptoms of schizophrenia and by not taking anti-Parkinsonian drugs regularly but only when they are needed to control some acute side-effects.

A word about side-effects

It is very unfortunate that so much of the public image of the use of drug medication in schizophrenia is based upon the idea that they act like a 'chemical straitjacket', reducing the individual to a zombie-like state where they can be more easily manipulated. This misconception must be partly laid at the door of those who, in the past, used heroic doses of neuroleptic medication so that sufferers were rendered permanently drowsy, apathetic and Parkinsonian. In addition, public opinion is now more critical of all medications, since many of them have been shown to have side-effects which, in a few cases, can be potentially serious. Moreover, there has arisen the suspicion that, in conditions such as schizophrenia, drugs are administered to aid management rather than for the real benefit of the patient's symptoms.

It is time, perhaps, to redress the balance. The neuroleptics, like most active medications, do have some side-effects, but the aim of treatment is to keep these to a minimum, and to abolish them completely if possible. Moreover, some of the symptoms, such as withdrawal and apathy, which have been attributed to the drug medication may be a direct result of the illness itself.

The test dose of a depot preparation should ensure that there is no individual hypersensitivity to that particular drug and maintenance doses can be kept as low as possible. Moreover, there is no reason to assume that someone will need to take medication indefinitely. It can be decreased and discontinued completely, provided the symptoms do not recur. Neuroleptics are intended specifically to relieve the distressing symptoms that schizophrenia causes. To be tormented by denigrating 'voices', to be suspicious even of those closest to one, to be unable to think clearly or to form relationships with other people, can hardly be seen as a happy state to be in. All the evidence is that neuroleptic drugs can substantially improve the quality of life for most schizophrenic sufferers and that, when properly used, they can do so without deleterious side-effects.

OTHER DRUGS

If your illness causes you to be very depressed for a period of time, **anti-depressant** drugs may be prescribed. These will consist of a course of treatment that will only be given for a fairly short time, and will be taken along with neuroleptic drugs.

If you are subject to episodes of depression followed by over-excitement, a drug called **lithium** may be prescribed, again to be taken with your neuroleptic drugs, in order to stabilise your mood. This drug must be taken exactly in the dosage prescribed since its effect depends upon the level that it attains in your bloodstream. Therefore you will be asked to come for regular blood checks to ensure that the level is correct. Lithium is a very effective medication in those who experience swings of mood and is very successful in the treatment of manic-depressive psychosis. However, some individuals who have mainly schizophrenic symptoms may also have difficulty in maintaining a stable emotional level and swing excessively into severe depression or great excitement. In other words, they show characteristics of both types of psychosis (this may be related to their genetic make-up). Often such individuals, whose ability to express emotion freely is well preserved, function very well in society once their mood swings are controlled, and it is for them that the combination of neuroleptic drugs and lithium may be very effective.

Other medications, such as **sleeping tablets** and **sedatives**, are rarely necessary for treatment of schizophrenia. If there is a temporary difficulty in sleeping, attention should be directed towards the reasons for this: excessive evening consumption of tea or coffee should be avoided; daytime activities increased; neuroleptic medication adjusted; and anxieties and worries discussed. The routine prescription of sleeping tablets or tranquillising medication should be avoided in schizophrenia, as in most other conditions.

Drugs to **control obesity** by suppressing appetite should never be taken, since they may produce or increase schizophrenic symptoms.

PSYCHOTHERAPY AND COUNSELLING

Freud, the pioneer of psychoanalysis, was firmly of the opinion that schizophrenia was an illness caused by physical factors, and hence unresponsive to psychoanalysis. Most experts now agree that psychoanalysis is contraindicated at every stage and in every type of schizophrenia, although of value in neurosis.

The reason for this contraindication is that psychoanalysis involves laying bare the defences built up to cope with a traumatic situation and which can produce neurotic symptoms. For example, a boy who is subjected to the painful divorce of his parents and whose mother keeps telling him how wicked his father is, builds up defences against this. A child needs to love and respect both parents, so he feels guilty and unhappy about denying his father and angry with his mother for forcing him to do so. At the same time, he is torn by his need for affection and care from her. He cannot deal with this complex mixture of emotions, and so they are repressed in an attempt to enable him to cope with life. But his conflict is unresolved, and the feelings that have been suppressed keep trying to break through the defences, like waves against a sea wall. Such feelings may be transformed into panic attacks, obsessional behaviour or failures in interpersonal relationships. He may be unable to establish a close relationship with someone of the opposite sex or experience irrational feelings of anger and hostility to his own children. In such a person, psychoanalysis would aim at exploring the past, so that he can realise why he is behaving in this way, and attempt to resolve his conflicts. It would not be a cosy series of chats, rather an often painful and stressful voyage of exploration, but in the end it can enable the person, who has been disabled by neurotic symptoms and who is motivated to change, to lead a much more satisfactory and happy life.

However someone with schizophrenia is much more vulnerable. There is no evidence that their delusions act as a defence mechanism: they would seem to stem from faulty perceptions and associations in the brain, and, indeed, by definition, they are not amenable to an appeal to logic or reason. It has been very tempting for some analysts to feel that a schizophrenic's delusions could be treated by methods such as reality testing; for example, a patient who had a delusional belief that his telephone was bugged would be asked to unscrew the instrument and examine it. But not finding anything would not convince the patient, who might merely say that a conspirator had removed the bugging device and would re-insert it later. A schizophrenic is able to incorporate everything into their delusional system. Schizophrenics need whatever defences they have to cope with their illness, and attempts to probe into traumatic experiences often result in severe agitation, worsening of the illness and may provoke a suicidal attempt.

Efforts have also been made to understand and explain the schizophrenic delusion and to try to find a way into the schizophrenic's world. There is no doubt that the form a delusion takes may depend upon the individual's past experience. Thus a boy who has been bullied at school and who later develops ideas of persecution may name his persecutors as the school bullies in disguise. So an attempt to understand why a delusional belief has taken the form that it has is very valuable. But the therapist should not fall into the trap of seeming to share it.

Many schizophrenics appear to have a part of them which recognises that they are ill. This possibly accounts for their frequent ambivalence. For example, a patient who is indignant at having to stay in hospital finds himself on an open ward from which he could easily depart. It is significant how rarely such a patient does leave voluntarily and how frequently they will wait for the doctor to make that decision. They angrily demand their discharge every time they see the doctor, but calmly accept the decision that they should remain in hospital. Nor is it uncommon for someone who is receiving a depot neuroleptic to complain bitterly about it and yet always turn up promptly for their injection. Therefore, it would seem most beneficial to the patient that their adviser should be not only sympathetic but also in touch with reality. Discussing delusions as if they were really true, as distinct from their reality in the mind of the patient, must only increase his or her bewilderment.

There is no evidence that more superficial psychotherapy, which involves talking to the patient about their problems and difficulties, can in any way cure the condition. This is not surprising in view of the evidence that schizophrenia is primarily a biochemical disorder. Although no one would deny the possible benefits of psychotherapy in helping a victim of leukaemia or multiple sclerosis to cope with their illness, equally no reasonable person would expect it to be curative. The idea that psychotherapy is a more appropriate treatment than the administration of drugs is certainly true for neurotic conditions, since there we are dealing with faulty ways of coping with stress. It is wise for such individuals to learn new attitudes rather than to suppress their symptoms with medication, which often turns out to be habit forming and ineffective in the long term.

The case in schizophrenia, in my opinion, is quite different. The opposition to neuroleptic medication often seems to be based on the idea of the brain as some kind of sacred organ, which should not be interfered with by organic means. Unfortunately, thinking, memory and emotions can be altered by many physical illnesses. No one would suggest that a brain tumour or meningitis should be treated by psychotherapy, and the fact that gross changes in the brain structure have not been demonstrated in schizophrenia does not mean that it must have a psychological origin. Brain function can be profoundly altered by biochemical disturbances which can occur, for example, when there are changes in the secretion of thyroid hormone or in diabetes.

The profound nature of the disturbance of mental functioning in schizophrenia, the intensity of delusions and hallucinations, the occurrence of catatonic symptoms, the fact that many schizophrenic symptoms can be reproduced by certain drugs and the consistently reported lack of response to psychotherapeutic intervention are all in favour of an organic causation.

However this does not mean that discussion of problems and

difficulties is not an invaluable part in the treatment of schizophrenia. The illness may be precipitated by stress, although it then seems to pursue an independent course, even when the stress is removed. And there is no doubt that disturbing events can, in some cases, produce a relapse or exacerbate the existing condition. Thus attention must be given to relieving stressful situations as much as possible and helping the individual and the family to cope with them. There is no point in returning a vulnerable individual to a situation which has already induced a breakdown unless it can be ensured that he or she will not be subjected to exactly the same stress again. For example, a medical student who has a schizophrenic breakdown would be well advised to consider thoroughly whether he or she could continue to cope, not only with a series of anxiety provoking examinations, but with a career in which there are constant physical, mental and emotional demands.

Psychotherapy for those at risk

Psychotherapeutic intervention can usefully commence in predisposed individuals, even before the appearance of the illness. Certain personalities are thought to be in more danger of developing schizophrenia than others; for example, a young person who is shy, retiring, incapable of making friends and who spends most of the time alone is more vulnerable than the outgoing extrovert whose life is full of hobbies and friends. Guidance in forming interpersonal relationships and a directing of adolescent energy and interest away from self-absorption to socialisation can only be beneficial. All too often the young adult who is found to be schizophrenic has a history of living alone, unable to find work, isolated from his family, spending all his time in one room and barely exchanging a word with anyone for weeks on end. It is true that such isolation may arise partly from the illness itself but, equally, the situation can only make the symptoms worse. It is important that families should retain contact with such vulnerable youngsters and not abandon them to their own devices, even though their behaviour may sometimes not be welcoming or encouraging.

Another group who are known to be at risk are the solitary people of middle age who live alone, have no friends and who become progressively more suspicious of everyone around them. Loneliness contributes to many psychiatric problems and it is important for community workers to try to alleviate this as much as possible.

Counselling

It is quite fundamental for someone who has or is recovering from a schizophrenic illness to find a counsellor that they can trust. This does not necessarily mean a doctor, although it should certainly be someone who has a sound knowledge of the illness. Many schizophrenics come to rely a great deal upon their community nurse or psychiatric social worker. Naturally, as in all friendships – and this is what such counselling should be – certain personalities get on better together than others and this individual variation has to be taken into account. The counsellor has to be able to accept the anger and the resentment which some schizophrenics understandably feel from time to time. This can sometimes be hard for those in the medical or nursing profession, accustomed to gratitude and deference, but it is really no different from the way that anyone with a disabling illness feels. The attitude 'Why me?' is not uniquely confined to schizophrenics.

Discussion of the problem should be related to the 'here and now' and attention given to practical matters – finding work, education, marriage, pregnancy, coping with the family. Most schizophrenics, except when it comes to relating a delusional system, are not given to great outpourings of their soul and are usually refreshingly eager to get on with their life, albeit on their terms.

Diana comes with her fiancé. She is on neuroleptic medication and wants to get married. She wants me to tell her future husband about her illness and asks about the possibility of pregnancy. She is anxious about the effects of the drugs, what might happen when she stops medication, and how she will be able to cope with her baby. She and her future husband are also concerned about whether the baby would ultimately become schizophrenic – her mother-in-law has said that this is almost inevitable.

Help here has to be directed to an assessment of Diana's need for medication, explanation about her illness to her future husband, a discussion about all the issues which pregnancy involves and an explanation of the genetic risks.

John is applying for jobs and wonders how to answer the inevitable question about a history of psychiatric illness. He has no recourse but to answer honestly, but a letter may help to explain how well he is now. Problems like those of John can only be satisfactorily solved when there is a better understanding and awareness of schizophrenic illness.

Wendy has made a complete recovery from a schizophrenic illness which occurred after she had her first baby. This has frightened her and her husband very much; they want to have more babies, but are fearful of a recurrence.

Wendy can be reassured that a further breakdown is not inevitable and that she can be supervised throughout her pregnancy. However, she and her husband have to be aware of the increased strain of looking after a second child, particularly if Wendy should fall ill again.

Oliver is a medical student. He wanted to study medicine mainly because most of his family are doctors. He had a schizophrenic breakdown in his second year, from which he eventually recovered. It is obvious that his heart is not in a medical career and that, moreover, it is too stressful an occupation for someone who is so psychiatrically vulnerable. He needs to be advised on alternative careers which will be less taxing and yet satisfying for someone of his intellectual ability.

Counselling for the family is just as important and time must be taken to explain the special problems of the illness, which they frequently find distressing and bewildering. The particular dificulties faced by them and the patient will be dealt with in a separate chapter (Chapter 9), but it cannot be too strongly emphasised how important it is to try to maintain a continuity of care in schizophrenia. By building up a relationship of trust, the individual will be enabled, when he or she improves, not only to come to an understanding of their illness but, most importantly, to rebuild their life and take advantage of their response to treatment and remission of symptoms.

GROUP THERAPY

This essentially consists of a small group of people, preferably eight to ten in number, who meet together to discuss mutual problems. The same criteria for psychotherapy applies for group therapy with schizophrenic patients – discussion should be directed towards immediate issues and not be allowed to degenerate into non-productive repetition of delusional preoccupations. One group may consist of sufferers themselves, another will be made up of parents and/or spouses, whilst in other cases the patients and relatives will be together. Included in the group, which is normally of mixed sexes, is at least one trained worker whose role it is not to monopolise discussion but to interpret and advise on the issues raised.

Groups conducted with those schizophrenics who are still distressed can be difficult, perhaps because the patients may not feel able to sit in the group or may be disturbed by their delusions and hallucinations. In many cases the illness itself renders them withdrawn and uncommunicative. However, even if the group does not appear to be progressing, there is often a real benefit in enabling a person to see that they are not alone in their illness. Some workers include less disturbed individuals, such as those with anxiety and depression, in their group, but such a group will require very careful handling because the less ill may be fearful of the lack of inhibition which the schizophrenics can show. Moreover, at their most ill, schizophrenics are not able to talk as coherently about life events as neurotics can.

Group therapy can be particularly beneficial as the schizophrenic illness responds to treatment, and especially so when there are patients at different stages of improvement. It can be heartening for someone just recovering from a breakdown to hear that another person is now well and back at home. Moreover, many of the apprehensions felt about neuroleptic treatment can be alleviated by discussion with someone who is responding to, and has remained well on, medication.

Groups of parents and spouses can also be invaluable. They gain mutual support and can provide advice about how they have each dealt with some difficult situation. Such groups do not need to be confined to a hospital setting and many families have an invaluable personal exchange of help.

As improvement progresses, the groups can become more

mixed so that all the family participates. Such groups can provide a source not only for discussion of problems but also, and just as importantly, for exchange of information about the illness and its treatment – for example, future research, new lines of treatment, diet, facilities in the community. Relatives, in particular, often gain considerable confidence from being able to chat freely to a professional in the field. All too often they find it hard to voice their worries in an outpatient clinic, but can do so readily in a more informal setting.

Group therapy should not be seen as a formal affair. In a number of community clinics recreational and cultural activities provide just as much therapeutic exchange as in a more organised setting. The presence of the professionals enables the patients and their families to see them as friends to whom they can more easily turn for help.

FAMILY THERAPY

In schizophrenia there is little place for the extensive exploration of family dynamics, such as might, for example, be appropriate in child psychiatry. Family interaction may be of great interest for research into the illness, but most families have enough to do in coping with their problems without being given the impression that the whole of their past life is being examined and possibly criticised. A diagnosis of a schizophrenic illness in a young person frequently gives rise to strong feelings of guilt, self-blame and anxiety. Parents tend to blame themselves, often quite unjustifiably, for the fact that their child is ill. There are, of course, a number of schizophrenics who come from disturbed homes, but a considerable proportion would appear to have had everything that a good parent can offer. The great majority of schizophrenics are children of non-schizophrenic parents and the illness may strike only one member of an otherwise stable family. Criminal behaviour and personality problems can be related much more directly to disturbed family relationships than can schizophrenia.

Family therapy should therefore be directed towards enabling the relatives to come to terms with the diagnosis and helping them to deal with the many difficulties they will undoubtedly face. It is neither kind nor fair to blame them for causing or perpetrating an illness which is still of unknown origin. Some workers, for example, have produced evidence to show that relapse amongst schizophrenics is greatest where the family show a high level of expressed emotion (see page 34), as measured by the degree of critical comment, hostility or emotional over-involvement that relatives display towards the patient. It may well be that it is the more disturbed patients who arouse the higher levels of expressed emotion, as those around find it increasingly difficult to cope. It may also be true that some families have little patience or tolerance for a sick member and tend to blame him or her for everything that goes wrong – a policy of 'scapegoating'. But this usually indicates that they have never been helped sufficiently to understand and to try and tolerate the patient's symptoms. Moreover, there frequently arises a vicious circle of over-protection and dependence on the part of the schizophrenic and the carer. A mother, for example, who sees her son neglected and not eating properly is bound to become more maternal and solicitous than she would to a healthy child of the same age.

The object of the family therapy must be, firstly, to enable the relatives to treat a schizophrenic in as normal a way as possible. They should be disabused of the idea that, because someone has schizophrenia, they are incapable of taking any decisions for themselves or returning to lead a normal life. Moreover, they should be encouraged not to see any slight deviation of behaviour as necessarily due to the illness without looking at the situation as a whole.

Secondly, their cooperation must be sought in relation to treatment. One cannot expect an ill person to persevere with a therapy which those closest are proclaiming to be useless. Relatives are often dismissed as 'hostile' because they are resentful and critical. This can be seen as a natural and defensive reaction to hearing the diagnosis of schizophrenia – very few lay people know everything about the illness until they have direct contact with it in a family member or friend. Therefore they need considerable help in realising that it is a treatable condition and one far removed from the ignorant mythology that has been built up around it.

Thirdly, relatives can play a vital role in rehabilitation. It is often more desirable for someone who has recovered from a schizophrenic illness to move into a community-based facility rather than remain in the parental home – this is a necessary part of growing up for most people. However, the active concern and support of the family remains crucial for the patient's subsequent progress.

Acceptance of a schizophrenic illness may be especially dificult for a spouse, especially when young children are involved. Close contact between the patient and his or her children should be maintained as far as possible; children, on the whole, are surprisingly able to adapt to all kinds of strange behaviour and do not necessarily see their parent as being so disturbed as might be expected. Psychiatric inpatient units now allow visiting for children quite freely. Moreover, the provision of mother and baby units means that a schizophrenic mother is not separated from her child at the very time when the bonding between them is so important.

Aims of family therapy

Attention in family therapy should thus be directed towards several aims.

- Creating a non-critical accepting environment.
- Having realistic aims for the patient. Work or an environment which involves serious stress cannot be beneficial. The family should accept that some of their previous ambitions have been unrealistic.
- Finding a happy means of social stimulation. Many schizophrenics are, by nature, rather shy and retiring. So are many other people, and nothing can be worse for someone with that type of personality than to be pressurised into constant 'jolly' activities; indeed, it would be counterproductive, causing more withdrawal. However it is also desirable that schizophrenics should mix with people who share their interests and hobbies. Thus a patient who enjoys sailing or fishing might well be happy to go with a friend to pursue these activities; the last thing he wants is a pleasure cruise, where a large number of people become drunk, vociferous, and force him to join them in what he sees as an embarrassing public dancing display.
- Learning how to respond to delusions and bizarre behaviour. The relatives should neither argue with the patient nor agree with the delusions. They must attempt to present a view of the real world by which the schizophrenic can measure his ideas.
- Finding a counsellor to whom they and the patient can relate.

- Avoiding subterfuges. Trust depends upon telling the truth in as kindly and thoughtful a way as possible. A patient may be angry if told that he is ill. He will be even more angry, and less trusting, if he suddenly finds that those closest to him have deceived him. If the relatives are concerned and feel they have to call for help, they should make it clear to the patient that this is what they have done. Any temporary anger is better than the nagging doubt that you can no longer believe what those close to you are telling you.
- Helping the patient's self-esteem and encouraging the maintenance of contacts with friends. All too often it is thought that it is better for the patient to be isolated until he or she is well. The truth is that it is necessary for someone with such a distressing illness to keep in touch with the real world as much as possible. Everyone who is ill feels pleased when others visit, write, telephone and express concern and sympathy – and schizophrenics are no exception.
- Actively participating in and understanding the proposed treatments.
- Obtaining an informed opinion and knowledge of the nature of a schizophrenic illness and the help that can be found in the community.

SOCIAL THERAPIES AND BEHAVIOUR MODIFICATION

Schizophrenia is an illness which produces social isolation and a decline in work performance. Most people feel happier when they are working and contributing something to society, and unemployment and redundancy can be a stressful time for a normal individual. Therefore many programmes for schizophrenics have developed the idea that adequately remunerated work should play a part in their rehabilitation. This has mostly taken the form of factory work, since this is more readily available and easier to organise, but there should be no reason why more intellectual pursuits should not be provided. An industrial rehabilitation unit, for example, can involve not only factory work but also typing, bookkeeping and catering skills. Unfortunately, at present it may well be difficult for the acquisition of these skills to lead to full-time work in the community.

An industrial rehabilitation unit.

However, the advantages of a work routine are invaluable in helping a person to see him or herself as part of the community. Attendance at a rehabilitation unit, communication with fellow workers and the feeling that something is being produced which is of social value, can raise a patient's self-esteem enormously. There is a world of difference between knitting dishcloths and undoing them again, and playing a part in making brightly coloured toys which are to be sold in high street toyshops.

Art therapy

Art therapy is used most often to help schizophrenics reveal their hopes and fears more freely in paintings and drawings than they can in conversation. Psychotic art has been the subject of considerable interest, especially as exemplified by world figures such as Van Gogh.

The main value for schizophrenics of activities such as painting seems to lie in the way in which it enables them to express profound feelings of doubt, fear and horror of the world around them. Some psychiatrists have suggested that excessive preoccupation with artistic expressions in schizophrenia may be disadvantageous, in that it encourages a further escape from reality, but there is little doubt that a number of patients are helped by being able to clarify otherwise inexpressible feelings in this way.

Schizophrenic paintings often show a fragmentation of subject matter, so that figures and objects become distorted. There is frequently a bizarre sinister quality to the work, and the whole picture may convey an intense impression of dread, fear and suspicion. In the early stages of schizophrenia the paintings may have a poetic and semi-magical quality, and in states of ecstasy and excitement the 'wondrous vision' experienced by the patient is conveyed by intense and bright imagery. Whether or not painting and the allied art of music has any specific place in the treatment of schizophrenics, artistic expression of this kind is of great value, not only for itself but because it prevents the patient regressing into an apathetic state.

Behaviour modification

Certain forms of behaviour can be seen as socially unacceptable. If you cannot get up in the morning, you will never keep a job or fulfill educational requirements. If you do not wash, people will not want to associate with you. In behaviour modification, therefore, patients and staff enter into a contract by which the elimination of such behaviour is rewarded. This, of course, has to be carefully planned so that patients who are still incapacitated by their illness are not made worse by excessive expectations. Moreover, the staff must not fall into the trap of thinking that everyone has to accept their social norms.

However, if one wishes to be accepted in society one has to

conform to certain rules and that is what behaviour modification, and the teaching of social skills in general, is aiming to achieve.

DIET

Control of disease by means of a change in dietary habits has become of great interest in many illnesses. Sometimes the results are excellent, whilst in other conditions the extent of the benefits produced by an alteration of diet still remains unproven. This is not to say that we would not all be healthier if we introduced more vegetables, wholegrain cereals and fruit into our diet, at the expense of large quantities of sugary and fatty foods. Certainly this is true of schizophrenia, where economic problems and lack of interest in preparing nutritious meals can lead to vitamin deficiencies, malnutrition or obesity.

The gluten-free diet

Interest has recently centred on the value of a gluten-free diet in schizophrenia. In a childhood condition called coeliac disease the inability to absorb gluten – a protein contained in wheat and other cereal grains – from the intestine, leads, if untreated, to severe diarrhoea, impaired physical development and psychiatric symptoms, consequent upon the failure of the gut to absorb vital nutrients. Some workers in the United States have noticed that there is a higher than average history of coeliac disease in those developing schizophrenia in adult life, and this has led to studies of cultures where maize and millet are used instead of the grains which contain more gluten and where there also appears to be a lower incidence of schizophrenia. It has subsequently been claimed that beneficial results in schizophrenic illness have been produced by a gluten-free diet, with the length of hospitalisation being reduced. It is suggested that wheat gluten can exacerbate the schizophrenic process and diminish response to treatment. The benefits of such a gluten-free diet are at present being investigated by the Schizophrenic Association of Great Britain.

There is no doubt, moreover, that excessive consumption of sugar and other refined carbohydrates such as white bread, biscuits and cakes can lead to fluctuations in blood sugar which not only cause hunger and increased desire for 'junk food', but also produce instability of mood and behaviour. The pages of slimming magazines are full of the sad stories of those who compulsively consume vast quantities of sweets, chocolates, chips and buttered rolls, and who continually feel not only bloated and overweight but tired, irritable and depressed. This vicious circle is a common cause of obesity – another problem which some schizophrenics complain about bitterly and which they tend to blame completely on the neuroleptic drugs prescribed for them.

Thus the plan of the gluten-free diet is twofold – to exclude not only gluten but also refined carbohydrates from the diet. To this end wholegrain brown rice, jacket potatoes, wholemeal bread, muesli, nuts, vegetables, fresh and dried fruit and an adequate amount of protein in the form of eggs, meat, poultry, cheese, fish and nuts are substituted for white flour, white rice, all processed breakfast cereals, white bread and rolls, cakes, biscuits and pastries.

Schizophrenics often drink many cups of coffee, probably for the stimulant effects of caffeine. However, like other stimulants, this results in a 'let down' effect afterwards, as well as habituation, so it is far from beneficial. Indeed, caffeine can make any individual who takes too much, jumpy, nervous and irritable. Decaffeinated coffee or coffee substitutes should be used. Additives in food should also be avoided as much as possible, since they have been incriminated as a cause of disturbed behaviour in predisposed people and especially in hyperactive children.

Thus a typical day's menu might consist of:

- Breakfast – a choice of
  muesli or yoghurt with fresh fruit
  boiled or poached eggs
  grilled lean bacon or ham
  tomatoes
  mushrooms
  wholemeal toast
- Lunch
  protein in the form of eggs, cheese, meat or fish
  large salad of raw vegetables
  potatoes or wholemeal bread
  fresh fruit

- Dinner
    a brown-rice dish
    stir-fry vegetables
    jacket potatoes with filling
    eggs, cheese, meat, fish
    fruits, or sweets made with brown-rice flour

There are a number of cookery books with suggested recipes in the appendix.

This diet is not an easy one to follow. For many people it constitutes a rather drastic change in eating habits and considerably more care in the buying and preparation of food. It would be a rather unusual individual who, living alone, was able to keep to it exclusively. However it is certainly worth a try, both for anyone with schizophrenic illness and for those who cook for them, either at home or in hostels or hospitals. Many of the suggestions could be incorporated into a diet for the whole family with beneficial results, since it is very healthy, appetising and satisfying. This family involvement is also much more likely to make the diet more acceptable to those schizophrenics who already see themselves as socially isolated and do not want to be on a special diet which only confirms them in this belief. The recipes could usefully be incorporated in cookery classes for those about to leave hospital who will have to cater for themselves in the community.

This is an interesting field of research, but no one is suggesting that this diet is a cure for schizophrenia. It is hoped, however, that not only will it lead to better general health and, therefore, a better chance of combating the inroads of the illness, but also to a lessening of disturbed behaviour. Marked fluctuations in blood-sugar levels produced by a constant diet of refined carbohydrate foods can only exacerbate the anxiety and tension often experienced in schizophrenic illness. It is commonsense, too, to realise that our brain functioning must be affected by the type and amount of food that we eat.

ELECTROCONVULSIVE THERAPY (ECT)

This is a treatment in which a brief and controlled electrical current is passed through the patient's brain while they are under the effect of an anaesthetic and muscle relaxant. There has been much controversy about this therapy, but most doctors, and many patients, would agree that it is a very effective treatment for severe depression. It is used rarely in schizophrenia, but can be helpful in cases where the condition is complicated by marked depressive symptoms which do not respond to other treatments.

Catatonic stupor

There is one – fortunately nowadays rare – complication of schizophrenia where ECT can be life saving, and that is in so-called catatonic stupor. Here the schizophrenic patient abruptly becomes completely motionless, unable to speak, eat or do anything for him or herself. The lack of nutrition and the possibility of complicating respiratory or other infections resulting from the immobility can be fatal if the condition is not rapidly alleviated.

Although the sufferer may appear to observers to be unaware of what is happening around them, this condition of catatonic stupor is not an alteration in the level of consciousness as such, but more a withdrawal from reality. Therefore it is likely that he or she is only too painfully aware of what is being said, and relatives, doctors and nurses must ensure that they do not say anything which will hurt or offend or make the condition worse. Moreover, this is not a condition which will respond to sympathetic management alone. Often the relatives, although seriously concerned, feel that they will be able to 'bring the sufferer around' by caring for them at home Unfortunately this illness requires prompt treatment with appropriate drugs to prevent serious and dangerous deterioration. Therefore it is vital to seek immediate medical advice.

If there is not a prompt response to neuroleptic medication, one or two electroconvulsive treatments will produce a great amelioration of the condition, enabling the patient once more to converse, move about and take nourishment. Catatonic stupor is a dramatic condition which, when effectively treated, usually progresses to complete recovery.

ALTERNATIVE THERAPIES

It will probably be clear by now that I do not feel that homeopathic remedies have any significant place in the treatment of schizophrenia. Hypnosis and acupuncture, whilst excellent treatments for suitable subjects, have not been shown to benefit most schizophrenics. They are difficult to hypnotise because of their lack of concentration, and they may also interpret hypnotic suggestions as part of their delusional system. The same is true of the use of needles in acupuncture. Possibly the cardinal rule is that one should do nothing to jeopardise the fragile balance between reality and the world of the schizophrenic's imagination.

It is understandable that those confronted with the undoubted drawbacks of orthodox medicine should look elsewhere for curative therapy. However at present there is no evidence that such a search is likely to be beneficial for schizophrenics. Despite this, therapies such as yoga and other relaxation techniques may well be helpful in alleviating the tension and anxiety frequently associated with schizophrenic illness, provided the individual is well enough to cooperate in practising them.

7

COMMUNITY CARE

INPATIENT HOSPITAL CARE

The most obvious situation where a schizophrenic illness can be treated is in a hospital. However, hospital admission is not always necessary and, where it is advised, should be for as short a duration as possible.

Admission to an inpatient unit may be advised when:

- there is a period of acute disturbance, when more intensive treatment needs to be given;
- when there is doubt about the diagnosis, and specialised observation and investigation are necessary;
- if there is a need to spend a little time away from a disturbing environment;
- if a period of rehabilitation is required to help re-establishment in the community.

Many of those with a schizophrenic illness can be treated by regular visits to outpatient clinics, a day hospital or a community clinic.

DAY HOSPITALS

Day hospitals may be attached to psychiatric inpatient units or be independent in the community. Ideally they should be in a central position, easily accessible for travelling to by public transport; it is highly desirable that those attending should, whenever possible, remain independent by making their own way there.

Attendance at a day hospital is invaluable for those who need assessment of and treatment for their illness, yet can be maintained with their families. This is particularly so for a young person with a first (and possibly only) breakdown, for whom removal from their familiar environment and their parents could be a very frightening experience. In the same way, a young mother who has had a breakdown can remain at home and in contact with her children, provided she has adequate support.

The other group who benefit from attendance at a day hospital are those who live in the community but who still need considerable help. Some may live alone and so enjoy the companionship, whilst others come to be involved in a work programme in an industrial therapy unit, in a clerical capacity or in another training facility.

Amongst the activities that a good day hospital will organise are individual and group therapy, family counselling, monitoring of any medication, therapies such as art, music and drama, a work or occupation programme, activities to encourage better health such as keep fit and relaxation, cookery classes and training in social skills by means of outings, shopping expeditions and so on.

COMMUNITY CLINICS

These centres provide a less formal setting for treatment than day hospitals. They are usually run by a community psychiatric nurse in association with one or more of the voluntary organisations such as MIND (the National Association for Mental Health). They of course help in the care of all types of psychiatric problems. Individuals can attend for social activities, to join groups or to see the nurse, the psychiatrist or social worker. There is often also an associated drop-in centre where people who are troubled, anxious, depressed or feel their illness is relapsing can come in and seek advice. This is invaluable because it provides immediate assistance for those who might well be reluctant to accept more formal referral. In addition, the fact that those with all types of psychiatric problem and of all age groups are attending helps to make a schizophrenic patient feel less isolated and more involved with others.

A drop-in day centre.

It is to be hoped that such clinics also provide a greater understanding for those in the community who know little about the illness.

INDUSTRIAL THERAPY UNITS AND SHELTERED WORKSHOPS

Industrial therapy units may be in the community or attached to a psychiatric hospital. They aim to provide a working environment similar to that found in a factory with clocking on and off, regular hours of remunerative work, proper meal breaks and, hopefully, a stimulating type of task. They serve a very valuable function enabling those who have lost the habit of a work routine to become accustomed to it again. Many who work in these units feel that they are contributing to society since the work is always of value and for sale in the open market.

Allowance is made for the worker's handicap, as they may find regular attendance, prolonged concentration and semi-skilled work difficult. Because of this the wages paid are correspondingly small, which can be a disadvantage, particularly for those living in the community as distinct from hospital inpatients. Moreover, it is very hard to provide more intellectual tasks, suitable for those who find routine factory work monotonous and unstimulating. Community clinics can often fulfill such needs by recruiting those recovering patients with special skills, for example in languages, art, music and physical education, for teaching in their group activities, but this usually has to be on a voluntary basis.

Sheltered workshops aim to function at a higher level of skills than industrial units and to train those with an aptitude for more complicated tasks. Unfortunately, with the present level of unemployment, those with a history of schizophrenia find it extremely difficult to move on and to obtain work. Young patients, however, may be able to take advantage of government training schemes or to continue their academic education.

LONG-TERM CARE

The old Victorian-type 'mental hospitals' had many disadvantages. They were often isolated from the centres of population, making visiting difficult, so that patients lost touch with their home, relatives and friends. Living in large groups, with little scope for individuality, led to the sort of institutionalisation which robbed individuals of initiative and interest in the outside world.

But there were some advantages. Often set in beautiful countryside, they provided the peace and tranquillity associated with the word 'asylum' – a place of sanctuary – as well as the companionship and support which many schizophrenics were unable to find in the world outside. And their closure, without adequate alternatives, has often led, not to improvement, but to worse conditions for the patients.

If people who have recovered from schizophrenic breakdowns can return to welcoming homes, this is obviously the ideal situation. Even so, for most of them there comes a time when it is necessary to increase their independence. Moreover, many do not have any home to which they can return, especially those who have spent several years in hospital. Lack of adequate provision can lead to them sleeping rough on the streets or going from one gloomy lodging to another. It is thus not surprising that many try to get readmitted to hospital.

It is very important that those who have recovered from a mental illness should return to their community, but it has to be accepted that a proportion do not make a full recovery and need continuing care. Efforts have been made to provide this.

Group homes

Group homes are ordinary houses in the community where small groups of patients live together, with greater or lesser degrees of supervision. Placement has to be judicious to ensure that the individuals will relate well to each other, but the group homes have on the whole been a great success. Many patients who have been in hospital for 20 or 30 years have been rehabilitated, to the extent that they can manage very adequately with cooking, shopping, finances and so on. Group homes also have the great advantage that people whose illness itself may make them socially isolated are not lonely.

Group homes are regularly visited by a community psychiatric nurse and/or a social worker who can advise on any difficulties. Should a resident require a short period of hospitalisation, his or her place in the home can be kept open. Many residents eventually graduate to homes of their own, get married and find employment.

Hostels

Hostels are larger communities, either for young individuals or for those who need rather more supervision than in a group home. They thus have more staff, and often a skilled psychiatric worker in charge.

Supervised lodgings and flats

Some hospitals have acquired flats for patients, whilst similar accommodation is available from the local authority. In addition, patients can go to live in rooms in houses run by those who have had psychiatric experience and who are tolerant and sympathetic to the problems of the mentally ill.

THE SHORTAGE OF LONG-TERM COMMUNITY CARE

Private individuals and voluntary organisations, such as the National Association for Mental Health, have played a big part in all these enterprises. However there remains a dearth of accommodation in the community, which leads to patients discharged from hospital finding themselves sleeping rough, or in bed and breakfast establishments where they are turned out to wander the streets all day with inadequate food and no opportunity for any worthwhile activity. Moreover, while it would seem desirable to close the large psychiatric hospitals and care for all the mentally ill in general hospital units, this does raise problems. Beds are at a premium in these smaller units and the tendency is to give priority to those with acute illness rather than to patients who need longer term treatment.

Whilst most patients with schizophrenic illness are able to live perfectly well in the community, a small proportion do find it more difficult. At present this can result in them being constantly in and out of hospital, with a consequent lack of continuity of care and with considerable distress for their relatives. As well as an increased provision of supervised small hostels in the community, it would perhaps be desirable to have some medium- and long-stay centres where those with severe and disabling symptoms, which do not respond greatly to treatment, can live in good surroundings where they can receive continuing care.

COMMUNITY CARE STAFF

Community psychiatric nurses

These nurses specialise in the care of the mentally ill in the community. They have had a full training in psychiatric nursing and take a special course in community care work. They liaise with the psychiatrist, the family doctor, the hospital and all those concerned in treatment. They are usually based in community clinics, but travel to visit patients in their homes as necessary.

For someone with a persistent disability from a schizophrenic illness, the community nurse may well be the most important link in therapy. He or she has the necessary skill to monitor the side effects of neuroleptic medication, to observe any evidence of relapse and to advise on simple physical problems.

The social work service

Social workers are trained professionals who can help patients and their families cope with difficulties. They can assist with housing and employment problems and help families to come to terms with the disability of one of their members. It is unfortunate that since the advent of generic social work, which involves every social worker dealing with all types of problems, as distinct from specialising, many of them have had little experience with the mentally ill. Moreover the increasing workload, both of child abuse and neglect and of the elderly infirm, has led to the problems of schizophrenics having a low priority, unless young children are involved.

It is particularly important, however, that a number of social workers should have specialised knowledge of psychotic illness, since they have an important role in the implementation of formal admission to psychiatric units under the 1983 Mental Health Act. Often they see the patient and family for the first time under these emergency circumstances, where it is difficult to form any kind of constructive relationship. In addition, heavy workloads and the present method of case referral may obviate any possibility of regular follow-up. In an ideal situation the community nurse and social worker should complement each other and work as a team.

The clinical psychologist

There is often confusion about the difference between a psychologist and a psychiatrist.

- A **psychiatrist** is a doctor who has taken a degree in medicine and then goes on to specialise in psychiatry – the study of disorders and diseases of the mind.
- **Clinical psychologists** have a degree in psychology – the study of human behaviour. They then specialise in the understanding and management of psychiatric illness from the point of view of both research and therapy. Since they are not medically qualified, many of them tend to be involved in the care of neurotic patients, who would benefit from psychotherapy or behaviour therapy. A number, however, take a particular interest in schizophrenia and are involved in diagnosis, rehabilitation, group work and, probably most importantly of all, research.

8

A GUIDE TO THE BENEFIT SYSTEM

It is a fact that many who are perfectly well mentally find it difficult to understand the workings of the benefit system in the UK. It is therefore reasonable to assume that those who are mentally not so well will find the system even more difficult to unravel. Here the assistance of a social worker or a community nurse can be invaluable.

It would seem that many schizophrenic patients and their families do not obtain all the benefits to which they are entitled, and a number are so bewildered by what they have to do that they cease to claim at all.

Here is a step by step approach to what you should do and how you should claim.

STATUTORY SICK PAY

The first thing to do is obtain a **sickness certificate** from your doctor.

If you are working for an employer and were earning enough to pay Class 1 National Insurance contributions (including married women's reduced rate contributions) you will usually get **statutory sick pay (SSP)** paid to you by your employer for up to 28 weeks. Send the sickness certificate to your employer.

In certain occupations, however, you will have an agreement with your employer to receive a particular rate of pay for a given length of time when you are ill. Again a sickness certificate will be required.

93

SICKNESS BENEFIT

If you are incapable of work by reason of illness and cannot get SSP from your employer, you can obtain **sickness benefit**, provided you have paid enough National Insurance contributions. The reduced married women's contributions do not count in this context, unless a woman is claiming because of an accident at work or an industrial disease. Sickness benefit is again paid for up to 28 weeks.

An important fact for schizophrenic patients is that they are still allowed to claim sickness benefit, even if they are doing work. The conditions are that:

- the work must be done under medical supervision (for example in hospital) or to improve the patients' health;
- the social security office must approve it in advance;
- earnings should not exceed a fixed limit.

Apply for sickness benefit on a claim form **SSP1E**, received from your employer.

You can also obtain sickness benefit if your SSP runs out before 28 weeks. Apply on claim form **SSP1T**, also received from your employer.

If you are unemployed, you are also entitled to sickness benefit for 28 weeks, if you have paid sufficient National Insurance contributions. Apply on a claim form **SC1** obtained from your social security office, doctor's surgery or hospital.

Benefits will normally be lower while a patient is in hospital. Always let the social security office know as soon as you are out of hospital, even if you only come out for a few days. The full rate of benefit can then be paid for this time, even if it goes down when you return to hospital. This is particularly important during periods of leave from hospital when you are recovering.

INVALIDITY BENEFIT

If you are still incapable of work after 28 weeks when your sickness benefit or statutory sick pay ends, you can claim **invalidity benefit**. You have to have paid the requisite number of National Insurance contributions, and the same earnings rule about work applies as for sickness benefit.

This benefit continues regularly while sickness certificates (which can be given for 13 weeks at a time) are provided. It is tax free and is not means tested.

SEVERE DISABLEMENT ALLOWANCE

If you cannot claim sickness benefit or invalidity benefit because you have not paid enough National Insurance contributions, you may be entitled to **severe disablement allowance (SDA)**. This is paid to people who have not been able to work for at least 28 weeks because of physical or mental illness or disability. If you get SDA you can be credited with National Insurance contributions. It is not means tested or taxed.

If you become incapable of work on or before your 20th birthday, you automatically qualify for SDA. If you first become incapable of work after your 20th birthday, you must prove that you are 80 per cent disabled; you are automatically accepted as 80 per cent disabled, for example, if you are in receipt of an **attendance allowance** (see below), this being the clause that applies most directly to schizophrenic illness.

Otherwise disability is assessed by a medical examination. In the case of mental disability, such examination will take into account:

- How much the disabled person can look after himself or herself, without being helped or prompted.
- How much he or she understands and responds to the surrounding environment.
- How the day is occupied.
- How much the carer has to do for them.

The guidance in the booklet *A Guide to Non-Contributory Benefits for Disabled People* points out that 'a disabled person who is capable of carrying out all the functions of everyday living, unaided, but can do so only when instructed and does not have the initiative to perform them without prompting, may well be assessed as 100% disabled' (p. 47). Obviously, there will be some schizophrenic sufferers who fall into this category, but finer gradations of disability in this condition are less easy to categorise than those for physical illness. In those patients whose illness fluctuates, case assessment will depend upon judgment as to whether the disability will improve or worsen. A claim is certainly worthwhile, because the examining doctor will also take into account specialist reports and hospital records. This is something that should be discussed with your doctor.

The rule of therapeutic work, in or out of hospital, up to a maximum earning level, that applies to sickness benefit also applies to SDA.

For claiming severe disablement allowance use the form in leaflet **NI 252** *Severe Disablement Allowance.*

ATTENDANCE ALLOWANCE

If a person is so mentally ill that they need considerable care from another person, **attendance allowance** can be claimed. It is a weekly cash benefit paid to them and not the carer. It is tax free and normally paid in full on top of other social security benefits. There is no need to have paid National Insurance contributions to obtain it, and it can be claimed even if there is no one to look after the person who is ill – it is based on the help they need, not on the help they are actually getting.

To qualify, an individual must – in the case of schizophrenic illness – be so disabled that for at least six months they have needed looking after by day or night or both.

- Looking after by day means that they must need continual supervision by another person throughout the day in order to avoid substantial danger to themselves or others. This would mean, in practice, prevention from lapsing into an apathetic uncared-for state or wandering from home and injuring themselves or other people.
- Looking after at night means that, for similar reasons, they need another person to be available for a prolonged period or at frequent intervals in order to watch over them. It is not sufficient that the other person is there merely to be woken up if necessary, so obviously this care at night would be more applicable in serious physical illness.

Attendance allowance has been awarded to a number of schizophrenic sufferers. Although it is to be hoped that with modern treatment there will be little necessity to claim such a benefit, because the illness will largely be in remission, there are certainly circumstances where a patient would qualify and where the benefit would be of considerable help to them and the carer.

Attendance allowance is about 50 per cent higher if you need to be looked after day and night than if you need to be looked after either by day or by night. Apply on claim form in leaflet **NI 205** *Attendance Allowance.* You can apply after three months of disability, although the allowance will not be paid until after six months – the so-called 'qualifying period'. However an early claim ensures that you receive benefit as soon as possible.

INVALID CARE ALLOWANCE

If you are a relative or friend and spending at least 35 hours a week looking after someone who gets attendance allowance, you may be able to claim **invalid care allowance (ICA)**.

You must be over 16 and under 60 if a woman, under 65 if a man, on the date you begin to qualify for invalid care allowance, but the allowance can continue wholly or partially after pensionable age. You cannot receive it if you earn more than a certain limit a week. Apply on the form in leaflet **NI 212** *Invalid Care Allowance.*

SDA and ICA overlap both with each other and with sickness or invalidity benefit, so that they are assessed together to produce the final payment.

For further details see leaflet **SB 20** *A Guide to Income Support* from DSS offices.

UNEMPLOYMENT PAY

A schizophrenic patient who becomes well enough to sign on at their local Jobcentre for work, and has paid sufficient National Insurance contributions, obviously becomes eligible for **unemployment pay** for a year. This can be given, along with **income support** in cases of financial hardship.

INCOME SUPPORT

This has replaced the old supplementary benefit scheme. It is a benefit given to those who do not have enough money to live on, a condition which qualifies many schizophrenics. It does not depend on National Insurance contributions, but is means-tested and taxable. There are certain conditions to qualify.

- You must be aged 16 or over.
- You and your partner must not be working for more than 24 hours a week.
- You must not have over £6,000 in savings.

The amount of income support awarded is decided by the DSS and depends on age, whether you have a partner and/or dependants, how much money you earn otherwise, and how much you have in savings. Of special interest to schizophrenic patients is the fact that, if you live in board and lodgings, a hotel, a hostel, a nursing home or a residential home, there are special rules for working out how much you can get.

Income support can be given on top of other benefits in cases of hardship or on top of earnings from part-time work. Along with it go free NHS prescriptions, dental treatment and glasses. It is also given to those who are sleeping rough, although they can only get the personal allowance and nothing for accommodation.

For further details see leaflet **SB 20** *A Guide to Income Support* from DSS offices.

COMMUNITY CARE GRANTS

These grants are given to help elderly or disabled people lead independent lives in the community. They may thus be awarded to those schizophrenics who are leaving long-term hospital care, in order to assist in their resettlement.

BUDGETING LOANS

If you have been having **income support** for at least 28 weeks, you may be able to obtain an interest-free loan to cover expenses for large items such as furniture, a cooker or refrigerator, household repairs or removal expenses. This is particularly useful for those schizophrenics who are setting up home in the community.

Budgeting loans are obtainable from social security offices (form **SF 300**) and are paid back on the basis of your income and circumstances.

NHS HOSPITAL TRAVEL COSTS

Those on a low income who need to visit hospital regularly or go as an inpatient may be able to obtain help with fares. Also, if you are regularly visiting a patient in hospital who is a close relative, you may be able to get help with travel costs if you receive **income support**.

Leaflet **H 11** *NHS Hospital Travel Costs* will explain this and application can be made at your local DSS office.

HOUSING BENEFIT

If you are on **income support** you will automatically qualify for the maximum amount of **housing benefit** from your local council. This means a payment of 100 per cent of your eligible rent and 80 per cent of eligible rates. Those who are not claiming income support can still get this maximum allowance if their income is the same or less than income support. You can qualify for housing benefit whether or not you are working, the level you obtain depending on your income.

If you claim income support, a housing benefit claim form will be automatically given to you. Otherwise, get a claim form from your **local council**.

SUMMARY

- Someone who develops a schizophrenic illness and who has paid adequate National Insurance contributions will be entitled to either **statutory sick pay** or **sickness benefit**.
- If they remain ill for longer than 28 weeks they become entitled to **invalidity benefit** and some of the other benefits listed.

- Those who have not paid sufficient National Insurance contributions will need to rely on **income support** and, subsequently, possibly **severe disablement allowance**.

It should be emphasised, however, that schizophrenic patients can recover well within 28 weeks and are then able to return to work.

POTENTIAL DIFFICULTIES

Schizophrenics do encounter a number of difficulties within the social security system. They may not recognise their illness immediately and therefore not get the requisite certificates in time, unless a relative acts for them. If they live alone, they may be too confused to appreciate the proper procedure for claiming benefits. Sometimes they land themselves in dire straits by tearing up their postal orders or losing, giving away or being robbed of their money.

In the acute stages of their illness, bizarre behaviour may strike alarm into the DSS staff who find it difficult to communicate with them. In addition, some schizophrenics are continually moving their place of abode or being frequently re-admitted to hospital for short periods of time, so that no one can keep track of them. It is in these circumstances that an understanding and patient relative, who will take over some responsibilities for the schizophrenic's financial affairs, can be invaluable.

9

LIVING WITH SCHIZOPHRENIA

UNDERSTANDING THE ILLNESS

It is vital that the patient and their relatives and friends have as great an understanding of the illness as possible. So many of the fears relating to schizophrenia are based upon ignorance and the foolish distortions that this brings about.

Schizophrenia is not a fatal illness. The majority of those who have had it can return to leading a normal or near normal life. A proportion have an illness which recovers within a matter of weeks and never returns. It is not physically disabling like a number of illnesses that can attack young people, such as multiple sclerosis and rheumatoid arthritis. Today there is much more understanding about the symptoms than in the past and many more sources of help. In particular, organisations like the National Schizophrenic Fellowship and MIND exist to help individuals and families with their problems.

I hope, in this chapter, to deal with many of the questions that patients and families may ask, but naturally each case is different and it is important to discuss serious decisions with your doctor, who will be aware of your individual circumstances.

EDUCATION

Schizophrenia may be diagnosed in the later school years or at university. How this will affect education will depend upon the severity of the illness and, most particularly, upon the effect that it has on thinking and intellectual performance. Where these are well preserved, there is no reason why a good academic attainment cannot be achieved. Certainly in an acute attack of schizophrenia, where there is complete recovery after a short-lived bout of the illness, an individual may proceed with their studies after a short period of time. Any drugs that are administered should not affect study, if they are given in reasonable doses and, particularly, as depot preparations.

Consideration has to be given to how keen the student is to continue with their studies and how interested they are in their future career. If the strain of studying and taking examinations is obviously too much, a different lifestyle will have to be planned; for example, there are many careers in which success and promotion depend on doing well in the work rather than in exams. However one also has to consider how much stress and responsibility the job itself will involve and how any future breakdowns will affect it.

Universities and colleges have doctors who have had considerable experience in dealing with psychological problems of students and who will be able to advise them about their future prospects.

EMPLOYMENT

A number of individuals with schizophrenia are able to continue in their normal occupations. Indeed, for those in any caring situation, the illness may give them a deeper insight into the problems of others. Ideally, a schizophrenic breakdown should be treated like any other illness and the schizophrenic's job should remain open until they are regarded as fit to return to work. Unfortunately this is an area where prejudice remains – it is certainly one of the areas to which voluntary organisations could devote more educational work. A number of employers are sympathetic and prepared to give a candidate a job on his or her merits, but to others the mere mention of any psychiatric problem seems to rob them of every judgment or human consideration. A schizophrenic whom I had treated, and whose illness was in such remission that she had obtained an upper second university degree, was turned down by numerous psychiatric hospitals for training as a nursing assistant, without even an interview, despite the fact that they were all starved of good candidates. Finally, one hospital was persuaded to accept her and she did extremely well.

A job has to be tailored to suit the individual personality. Someone who is shy and withdrawn is unlikely to make a good salesman, but may find a job in quieter surroundings, such as academic librarian, ideal. Many schizophrenics find difficulty in obtaining work because illness has interrupted their training. Here the disablement resettlement officer at the local employment office may be invaluable. He can suggest training schemes and courses depending on particular aptitudes. It is important to try to obtain a work record in this situation, so the effort should be made to take any temporary work, no matter how unskilled, in order to prove that you can hold down a job.

Seek advice also about how to present your previous illness to an employer, so that he can form a realistic opinion about what problems you have had. Your doctor, community psychiatric nurse or social worker will be able to assist you. Often they can talk to your employer, bearing in mind that many employers have had no experience of psychiatric illness and consequently have many apprehensions and misunderstandings about it.

There are some occupations, such as entry to the armed forces, where a history of schizophrenic illness would prevent admission. However, most jobs are open and the fact that you have had a schizophrenic illness does not mean that you will be an invalid for the rest of your life. Remember, too, that prejudice against employing those who have had a psychiatric illness will only disappear when the expatients prove that they can do a job as well as anyone else. So regard yourself as a pioneer and try not to be discouraged if you have a few setbacks.

A small group of schizophrenics, particularly those who have been hospitalised a long time or who have disabling symptoms, will find it very difficult to find employment in the open market. But work, and the feeling that one is contributing to society, are very important, and it is hoped there will be more provision of units where such people can work under relatively protected circumstances. Ideally, such units should have a much wider range of occupations than they are able to offer at present.

LEISURE

It is very important that everyone makes full use of their leisure, and this is particularly so in the case of an illness like schizophrenia, where making social contacts can sometimes be a problem. If solitary activities such as fishing, walking and reading are preferred, an effort should also be made to get involved in other areas where one can meet new people. For someone who is shy this can be a real ordeal at first, but it is often helped by attendance at a community centre where one is likely to come into contact with those who are more understanding. Many such centres now run training groups in social skills which teach you how to communicate better with others, how to overcome shyness and pluck up the courage to take up a new interest. Many people who have not been ill are also shy, so again it is wise not to let your illness be an excuse for withdrawing from society.

All relatively sedate leisure activities are quite all right for those who are on medication, provided there are no disabling side-effects. More adventurous pursuits such as sailing, skiing or mountain climbing should be discussed with your doctor; it is probably wise to avoid any potentially dangerous activities such as these on your own, in case there is any unexpected reaction to medication. In addition a very stressful situation may not be the best way to help your illness.

It is natural that you will not want to be preoccupied with your illness all the time, but it is worthwhile attending meetings of groups like the National Schizophrenic Fellowship, where you can find out more about recent advances and new ideas that may be helpful to you.

Alcohol

This forms part of most social occasions, but if you suffer from schizophrenia the rule is to be very careful how much you drink, confining yourself to a couple of glasses of wine or a pint or so of beer. This is for several reasons.

- Excessive consumption of alcohol is bad for anyone.
- If you are taking any medication this may make the effect of alcohol more marked.
- Possibly most important, alcohol in excess can release considerable emotional feelings such as anger, depression

and frustration in anyone, which could reactivate the symptoms of your illness or make them worse.

It is wise not to use alcohol as a crutch to prevent you facing reality; if you do you will only find yourself with more problems. A hangover the next day, for example, will make it harder for you to get to work on time and function efficiently. Alcohol-induced arguments with those nearest you can only jeopardise the relationship you have with them.

If you are tempted to drink too much, it is wise to stop having alcohol altogether for a while so that you can show yourself that you can control your drinking.

Cigarettes

There is nothing to recommend the practice of smoking cigarettes – they are a major cause of premature death and they cost a lot of money. The practice of giving cigarettes to patients in psychiatric hospitals in order to 'make them feel at ease' is therefore to be greatly deplored. Certainly, though, many schizophrenics do smoke excessively, probably for some kind of stimulant effect.

The best advice is not to start at all. However, failing that, it is not impossible to give up. If you cannot cut down cigarettes on your own, go to one of the anti-smoking clinics that will probably be available in your area. It may seem that you have enough problems without worrying about your smoking, but you should not allow yourself to drift into continuing a habit which can only cause you ill-health and add to your problems. Moreover, excessive cigarette smoking is liable to make you feel jittery and tense.

Illegal drugs

These are to be avoided at all costs, because, as I hope I have made clear, they can make your illness worse. All appetite suppressant drugs should also be avoided, because they too can produce psychotic symptoms in predisposed people.

Travel

There is no reason why someone who has had a schizophrenic illness should not travel anywhere they want, although a few precautions are necessary.

• If you are on medication, make sure you have a supply,

since your drugs may be very expensive or unobtainable abroad.

- Have a note from your doctor for the customs, in case you are stopped, since they may be suspicious of your medication.
- Also have a note to a doctor in the country to which you are going, stating the dose of any medication and when injections are required.
- Find out before you travel which countries have reciprocal health arrangements with the United Kingdom. This means that, if you unfortunately become ill, you can receive free treatment.

Some countries, such as the United States, have very high costs of medical treatment and it may be difficult to obtain enough insurance to cover this. It is preferable, under such circumstances to go to visit friends or relatives rather than embark on a journey around the country completely alone.

If you are applying for insurance for overseas travel, you have to state that you have been ill, otherwise, if you have a recurrence whilst you are away, the insurance is invalidated. This applies to every pre-existing illness and is not unique for schizophrenia.

Driving

A schizophrenic illness should not necessarily prevent you from continuing to drive. Naturally, driving a car is prohibited if you are temporarily on large doses of medication which make you drowsy. However, receiving medication in itself does not render you unfit to drive.

If you are on permanent medication, you have to declare what drugs you are taking to the Motor Vehicle Licensing Authority and have a medical examination to ensure that you are not rendered incapable of proper concentration by the effects of your illness or your medication. Failure to do this could lead to prosecution and would certainly invalidate your insurance in case of an accident. In practice, many patients on medication are able to continue to drive their cars. Again, those restrictions are not unique to schizophrenia; they apply to everyone on long-term medication and to anyone with conditions such as epilepsy, defects of vision and certain heart abnormalities. This again is a matter which should be discussed with your doctor.

WEIGHT

A number of schizophrenics who are on medication put on weight and then blame their tablets or injections for this. Some even use the weight gain as an excuse for discontinuing their drugs.

It may be that medication plays some part in weight gain, but it is mainly a poor diet which is responsible. In those who live alone, excessive consumption of take-away foods such as fish and chips, sugar-laden soft drinks and coffee can lead not only to obesity but also to nutritional deficiencies. A healthy diet is given in this book (see pages 79–81) and should help those who wish to maintain a reasonably ideal weight.

Again, losing weight is not easy. Particularly during periods of loneliness and unhappiness, it acts as a consolation to have chocolates, cream cakes or calorie-laden snacks. This is why it is important to learn how to cook tasty balanced meals and to keep occupied so that food ceases to be so important. Moreover, try to have snacks such as chopped vegetables or fruit as a substitute for high-calorie food.

Similarly, the problem of those who are seriously under-weight should also be manageable with a good nutritious diet.

MARRIAGE

A number of people are already married when they develop schizophrenic illness. Others who develop the illness in adolescence or early childhood, particularly men, do not marry, probably because of difficulties in forming emotional relationships. However there is no reason why, with proper guidance, someone who has had a schizophrenic breakdown cannot marry and bring up children with the same hope of success as anyone else.

You may be perfectly well when you meet the person you want to marry. The temptation is to say nothing about any past problems. In my opinion this is unwise. It is possible that you may have another breakdown – in the case of a woman this could occur after childbirth. You will then need the support of an understanding partner, who is likely to be very hurt if he or she feels you have not been truthful. In addition, in a good relationship there is no reason why a history of psychiatric

107

problems should make any difference; if it does, it is much better to realise this before marriage rather than after. Questions such as having children or moving to work abroad are matters which will have to be given special consideration if you have had psychiatric problems, and it will be much better for you and your future spouse if you are able to have advice together.

Of course, if you still have some symptoms and are on medication, your partner is more likely to be fully appraised of the situation. Sometimes two people who have both had psychiatric problems meet and decide to marry. Again, they have to be aware of the added stress that an exacerbation of their illness might bring about and be able to accept that they may need extra help in such a situation.

Parents who have a schizophrenic child may feel overprotective when the young person makes relationships with the opposite sex. This is often from the best of motives, to protect the patient from being hurt or assuming too much responsibility. However, it is important that anyone who has had a schizophrenic breakdown should be enabled to lead a normal life like everyone else, and this includes creating a close relationship with a partner.

HAVING CHILDREN

It is the feeling that schizophrenia is an inherited condition that makes many people opposed to the idea of a schizophrenic having children. The genetic risks have been clearly set out in Chapter 3 and this is something that must obviously be discussed when marriage is proposed. Some couples may feel the risks are too great and may decide not to have children. Others may feel that the risk is worth taking. It should be remembered, as mentioned elsewhere in this book, that many schizophrenic illnesses occur in individuals with no family history. Moreover, no one is completely sure of their genetic endowment and many conditions come out of the blue into a family who have regarded themselves as healthy.

Whether or not it is desirable for a couple to have children must depend upon the severity of the schizophrenic illness, its incidence in other family members and how far they are able to cope with raising a family. They should be aware that a schizophrenic illness can occur after childbirth, although not invariably so. There is no very adequate way of predicting this, although of course careful monitoring during pregnancy can only be beneficial. Moreover, such illnesses usually respond well to medication and there is complete recovery.

Where a schizophrenic illness arises for the first time after childbirth, the outlook is just as good. It is again impossible to predict whether a further pregnancy will be followed by a recurrence; sometimes a schizophrenic breakdown in the first pregnancy may be followed by one or two quite normal deliveries with, say, a further breakdown in the fourth. However, if there have been two successive breakdowns then a further pregnancy would be inadvisable.

It is probably wise for those who have had one or more schizophrenic breakdowns to limit their families. This is because the stress of bringing up children may not be beneficial for someone liable to have psychiatric problems. For a woman a recurrence of her illness may mean a period of separation from her family, while for a man it may mean interference with his work prospects and consequent economic difficulties.

The whole question of having children should therefore be discussed, preferably before marriage, and all the options should be made clear. Advice also has to be given in those cases where the schizophrenic breakdown occurs for the first time after childbirth (see below).

Pregnancy

In someone who has had a schizophrenic breakdown but who is now not on medication, pregnancy is not a problem as schizophrenic recurrences are very rare during pregnancy. There are more problems when the prospective mother is on medication. There is no evidence that the neuroleptic drugs are implicated in producing foetal abnormalities, but that is a natural concern on the part of those involved. Ideally all drugs should be avoided in the first three months of pregnancy when the foetus is developing, and in those schizophrenics who are on medication and are contemplating having a baby it is wise to reduce the dose of medication to as low a level as possible and discontinue it for as long as possible if this can be managed. It can then be recommenced, if necessary, after delivery.

Cooperation with your doctor is most important at this time.

Schizophrenia does not lead to any particular problems in pregnancy or delivery and there is no reason why your baby should not be born quite normally.

However it is wise that your obstetrician should know of any problems in case difficulties, which may require medication, arise during labour.

Schizophrenia is not in itself a reason for termination of pregnancy. This would only be considered if the mother felt that she was in such circumstances that she could not cope with a child. It also has to be remembered that the stress of a termination may itself precipitate a recurrence of a schizophrenic breakdown.

Schizophrenia developing after childbirth

This is usually an acute illness developing a few days after delivery. Warning signs are the fact that the mother often becomes very overactive, she cannot cope adequately with the baby and may develop a preoccupation with delusions that increase this difficulty. Sleep is disturbed and there may be rejection of the husband and the family. Despite this, many mothers remain very concerned about their baby, often to the extent that they are fearful that there is something wrong with it, despite all reassurance. This is obviously an extremely distressing state for the husband and family – what should have been a happy event has become a tragedy. They can be reassured, however, that complete recovery is normally the rule.

Where there is family support, it may be possible to treat the patient at home. However, it is essential that someone takes responsibility for the baby, this often being best achieved in a mother and baby hospital unit. So that bonding is maintained, the mother and her baby should be kept together – the days when such patients were snatched into hospital and did not see their child for weeks are mercifully past. Nothing can be more distressing for someone, already mentally disturbed, than not to be able to see her child. It is also usual, after the first few days, for the mother to be able to take over the full responsibility of caring again.

Any other children should not be forgotten. They do not want to be made to feel that the new baby has not only made their mother ill but also separated them from her. Therefore visiting the hospital with their father is very important. When the mother is improving, short home visits can be arranged so that she can be with her family in the home environment. It is possible in some circumstances to have a family home help for the patient when she returns home so that she can make a gradual adjustment to her new role.

Breastfeeding
There is naturally no problem with breastfeeding if the mother is not receiving medication. However certain drugs pass into the breastmilk and can make the baby drowsy, so if such medication is really necessary it might be better for the baby to be bottle-fed. A number of mothers have a great wish to breastfeed their babies and feel very let down if they cannot, so under these circumstances a change of medication to a drug that is not secreted into the breastmilk can be considered.

Contraception
Acceptable contraceptive methods are a matter of individual preference. None of the medications prescribed for schizophrenic illness interferes with the taking of the contraceptive pill. For someone who has difficulty in remembering to take pills regularly or cannot cope with barrier methods of contraception, the use of the coil can be considered. Some form of sterilisation may be indicated if the couple feel that they definitely do not want any more children, but it has to be remembered that in most cases this is an irreversible decision.

MARITAL PROBLEMS

Naturally, someone who has had a schizophrenic breakdown may have similar marital problems to anyone else. But, there are some problems that can occur in response to the symptoms of the illness itself. Withdrawal from social contact and inability to cope with everyday life may often be even more of a problem for a spouse than for parents, since a husband or wife is so much more dependent on the companionship of their partner. It is here that family group therapy may be of great help.

A schizophrenic illness in one partner can certainly be very alarming for the other partner, who sometimes feels to blame, particularly if the illness occurs after childbirth. And when it comes out of the blue, there may be great difficulty in understanding the symptoms. A husband who comes home continually to find the home in disarray and a wife who is paranoid against him is bound to be bewildered. Similarly, a wife whose husband becomes withdrawn and emotionally cold may initially not suspect an illness but the advent of 'another woman'. The unaffected partner has to be given help to understand that the one who is suffering from schizophrenia behaves as they do not out of some deep-seated malice but because they are ill.

It is wise, however, to avoid the temptation to blame everything on the illness. It is natural that any differences might be interpreted as a sign of the illness returning and the doctor called in with the information that the patient is relapsing. But care should be taken to see things from the point of view of the patient, since nothing can be more deleterious for them than to feel that their normal reactions are being misinterpreted. The professionals should also ensure that they give the marital partner the understanding and support they deserve.

One of the best illustrations of how schizophrenia should *not* be managed is given in the novel *Mrs Dalloway* by Virginia Woolf, who herself suffered throughout her life from a series of manic depressive breakdowns. Septimus Warren Smith has become mentally ill after his experiences in the trenches in the 1914–18 war and the death of his friend Evans on the last day of fighting. He has progressively sunk into a schizophrenic state, which neither his wife nor doctor understand. In a brilliant portrait, all his symptoms are described. He writes reams of paper full of nonsense, he feels that the human voice can quicken things into life under certain atmospheric conditions, imagines that his friend Evans is hiding somewhere and is not really dead, and is afraid of the hostile glances that he feels everyone gives him. Sir William Bradshaw, a Harley Street specialist who should give any psychiatrist cause for thought, is called in. In a wonderful portrayal, he is described as trying to prove to the patients that he, Sir William, is master of his actions and they are not. His suggested cure is to commit Septimus to his nursing home in the country where he can be taught 'a sense of proportion'. His wife is desperately trying to understand the change in Septimus and, ironically, she is just beginning to feel closer to him when the doctor arrives to take her husband away. No attempt has been made to explain his illness to either of them; they have merely received the impress of Sir William's will as he 'swoops and devours'. Septimus becomes acutely paranoid, fearing that he will be killed. He does not want to die, but in his terror he flings himself from his window and is killed. As an example of how not to treat a schizophrenic and his family the book cannot be bettered, and it is invaluable reading for those who would like to understand what it must feel like to have schizophrenia.

PROBLEMS FOR THE RELATIVES

Withdrawal from social contact

This may be particularly marked in certain types of schizophrenic illness which do not respond adquately to medication and it is the symptom with which many relatives find difficulty in coping. The withdrawal may take many forms. The individual may become terrified of leaving the house. They stand alone at family parties, unable to make conversation. They withdraw to their room and refuse to come out, but become bitter and resentful if their relatives go out without them. They may chain-smoke, be unable to occupy themselves, talk to themselves and sleep excessively. Sometimes they refuse their medication or hide it; at other times they give rise to concern by being excessively trusting and naive with strangers, or asking embarrassing and socially inappropriate questions.

Under those circumstances it is important that a regular routine is established at the early stages of the illness. The patient should have a programme of activities during the day, for example attendance at a day centre or industrial unit. They should be allocated household tasks as if they were well. The consequences of any inappropriate social behaviour should be explained to them. Many relatives find that a direct approach does not always work; thus the patient may accept a clean set of clothes if these are left hanging in their room rather than actually offered to them. They should be made to feel a responsibility for managing the household, and asked to do shopping for meals that they will prepare. It has to be accepted that sometimes they will make mistakes or do things such as housework inadequately. If there are considerable difficulties at home it may be desirable for there to be a period of inpatient rehabilitation.

It would appear that, in this form of illness, the apathy becomes almost like a vicious circle. The patient has no stimulation and insufficient initiative to take up any interest spontaneously. This reinforces the idea that they have nothing to do, so they drift into a state of boredom. It is important to try to break this circle by introducing new interests as much as possible, encouraging participation in outside activities and contact with new people. Some schizophrenics find it easier to talk to others who have had a similar illness because they feel that they can obtain more understanding; this should not be discouraged, since the patients are more likely to help each other rather than make each other worse.

Try to maintain contact with the community psychiatric nurse and try to ensure that there is a continuity of care. If the patient can form a good relationship with such an understanding professional, they are much more likely to accept advice. Moreover, the community nurse will be able to advise on how you can handle a particular situation. Those who are afraid to leave the house, for example, may well be more willing to do so if they can make friends with someone who will call for them and accompany them to a social occasion.

It is wise to avoid treating the patient as if they were seriously ill and making undue allowances for their behaviour because of this. It is very easy for anyone to sink into an invalid role; Elisabeth Barrett Browning and Florence Nightingale, two formidable women, spent a great deal of their lives reclining on sofas convinced that they were too weak to move. It is all the more easy for someone who does have psychiatric problems to give up and resign themselves to chronic illness. But the fact that this need not necessarily be so is illustrated by the profound changes that take place in 'institutionalised' patients when some stimulation and interest is added to their lives. Support groups are excellent in this respect, since the relatives of other patients may have found solutions to the same problems you are facing.

Depression and suicidal ideas

These symptoms can be very distressing when they occur as part of the illness. However, contrary to popular belief, talking about the depressive feelings is likely to act as a relief rather than the reverse; sometimes such feelings are temporary, merely occurring in response to some setback, and can be relieved by discussion and sympathetic understanding.

At other times, though, the problem is more deep seated and will require medical intervention; this should be suspected if the mood is not alleviated by talking about the problems and where it is either inappropriate to the circumstances or a part of irrational depressive ideas. Thus, if someone is depressed because they are convinced they are dying of cancer, despite reassurances about their health, or because they feel that they are so evil that they are not fit to live, the depression is very severe indeed. There may also be marked sleep problems and loss of appetite. In such cases your doctor should be consulted immediately.

It is important, also, continually to reassure the patient that all will be well, even if they do not seem to accept what you are saying. Many depressed individuals in fact cling to this hope and are helped when others reiterate it.

Coping with other symptoms

Many schizophrenics feel the need to explain their irrational ideas to others. If the relatives are brusque, the patient feels that they do not understand and inevitably becomes more withdrawn. The patient should therefore be allowed to talk freely. There is no point in arguing about their delusions, just as there is no necessity to reinforce or ridicule them either. It is desirable to try to point out that possibly not everything is as the patient sees it.

Fortunately, medication is usually quite effective in reducing these particular symptoms. And as the abnormal ideas regress, it is time to help the patient return to reality. This can be done by asking them to relate their abnormal experiences, the hearing of voices or an unfounded suspicion, so that the carer can discuss it with them and try to provide a reasonable explanation. The recovery from such a paranoid illness may be marked by considerable doubt and anxiety. Naturally, some of the bizarre ideas have great reality for the patient, but as they get better they will come to appreciate the abnormality of their ideas.

It is also beneficial to make an effort to understand why the patient has developed the type of delusion that they have. Often delusions express some fear or anxiety which the sufferer will need to overcome when they are well; for example, a person who has always felt inferior to others and has a very low self-esteem may well, when they become ill, develop ideas that everyone is laughing at and mocking them.

Involving the family

Explain the illness to the rest of the family as clearly and simply as possible. If you feel you cannot do this yourself, ask a professional to do so. One of the difficulties that many family members have is realising that behaviour which upsets or annoys them is due to illness rather than deliberate intention. Siblings cannot understand why their brother or sister ignores their friends or is rude to them from time to time. Children feel that their mother or father does not love them because sometimes they are preoccupied and do not show spontaneous affection.

Those around should be encouraged to help the patient and to cooperate in promoting their recovery. Children in particular seem to be able to develop understanding and practical support without putting undue emotional pressure upon a sufferer. It is essential for families to avoid the high expressed emotion which has been implicated in relapse of the illness (see page 34).

Violent behaviour

Despite popular opinion to the contrary, violent behaviour of any severity is rare in schizophrenics – they figure very little in the statistics for violent crime. Indeed most patients are extremely timid, dislike any show of anger and are sometimes very distressed by any irritability or show of anger by their relatives.

The majority of violent acts, such as they are, occur when patients are fearful and feel that they have to defend themselves. Thus, someone who is suddenly removed to hospital without any discussion may well pick up a chair and throw it down again. Such occasions can be avoided by treating the patients with tact, respect and honesty.

Compulsory admission

Regrettably, this may sometimes be necessary if a patient is so ill that they are unable to have any insight. Quite naturally, many relatives are reluctant to initiate such a procedure, fearing they will be blamed by the patient later. Under these circumstances it is probably preferable for an approved social worker to make the application.

It is obviously much more desirable that someone who has had a relapse of a schizophrenic condition agrees to accept treatment as an informal patient. They can often be persuaded to do this if sufficient time is allowed for discussion and no one panics about the situation. Moreover, things are made easier if there is a relationship of trust and affection with the relative. They have a difficult role in that they have to be supportive to the patient but at the same time firm in their belief that he or she is not well and needs further treatment. It may be of some consolation to know that most patients who are compulsorily admitted do not bear any grudge as they improve, because they realise that they were unwell.

10

LEGAL MATTERS

THE MENTAL HEALTH ACT 1983

The ideal way for someone suffering from schizophrenia to be treated is on an informal basis – that is, with their full consent and cooperation. Unfortunately, due to the loss of insight that can occur during the course of a schizophrenic illness, a patient may temporarily refuse to accept that they are ill or that they need treatment. In those circumstances, and where there is a threat to the individual's health and safety or that of the others, compulsory admission to hospital may be necessary.

The Mental Health Act of 1983 is designed to strike a balance between the accepted need for such admission in certain cases and the civil liberties of the patient. Everyone is agreed that the patient should be treated on an informal basis as soon as his or her condition allows it, and it is frequently the case that, after a short period of treatment, insight and acceptance of the illness is regained.

The Act defines four specific categories of mental disorder:

- **mental illness**, the group into which schizophrenia obviously falls;
- **mental impairment**;
- **severe mental impairment**; and
- **psychopathic disorder**.

The Act is quite definite that a person may not be dealt with as suffering from mental disorder purely by reason of prom-iscuity, other immoral conduct, sexual deviance or dependence on alcohol or drugs. There has to be an associated mental illness as, for example, where the presence of a schizophrenic illness may cause the sufferer to take refuge in an over-indulgence in alcohol or dependence on stimulant drugs.

A person who is ill and thought to require admission may be taken to hospital under various sections of the Act.

Section 4 – admission in emergency

This section provides for admission in an emergency and for a period of 72 hours only. Application must be made by an approved social worker or the patient's nearest relative, with the recommendation of one doctor who does not need to be a psychiatrist but who should preferably know the patient well and who must have examined him or her within the past 24 hours. It is made quite clear that this section should only be used in an emergency, where it is impossible to wait for a second opinion.

Section 2 – admission for assessment

This allows for admission to and detention in hospital for assessment, followed by medical treatment, for a period of up to 28 days, when a patient is suffering from a mental disorder of a nature and degree which warrants this and when he ought to be so detained in the interest of his own health and safety or with a view to the protection of other persons. Application can be made by an approved social worker or by the nearest relative, with the recommendation of two medical practitioners, one of whom must have been accepted as having special experience in psychiatry.

All those concerned must personally interview the patient and provide grounds for their recommendations in writing. It is not sufficient to say, for example, that a patient suffers from schizophrenia and 'appears to be hearing voices'. A schizophrenic illness is not, in itself, ground for detention. There has to be evidence that, if the patient is not detained in hospital, the health or safety of the individual or of other people will suffer. Because someone has paranoid delusions and haunts official buildings with their complaints does not in itself make them a fit subject for dealing with under section 2. However, if it is felt that further diagnostic assessment would be helpful, if their health is deteriorating due to self-neglect, if it is likely that neuroleptic treatment would be beneficial in alleviating their delusions or that they are likely, because of their ideas, to threaten or harm others, it is a different matter.

The majority of those admitted under section 2 improve sufficiently with treatment to be discharged or to become informal before the expiry of their section.

Section 3 – admission for treatment

The criteria for this section are that the patient is suffering from a mental illness which must be of a nature and degree that makes it appropriate for him or her to receive treatment in hospital. The criteria are not satisfied if the treatment could be given just as well in the community or under guardianship. Treatment need not be expected to cure the patient's disorder, but either to alleviate it or to prevent it becoming worse. It must also be necessary for the health and safety of the patient and/or for the protection of others that he or she should receive this treatment.

The procedure for the application is the same as for section 2, but section 3 lasts for six months and can be renewed at the end of this period provided the criteria still apply. In cases where a section 2 patient still obviously requires treatment which he will not accept on an informal basis, section 2 can be converted to a section 3.

Patients on section 2 and section 3 may be given leave at the discretion of their doctor. One of the problems that has given rise to difficulties with section 3 patients is the clause that they need to receive treatment in hospital. Some psychiatrists feel that a patient who is discharged into the community on a stable level with medication would be more likely to continue the medication if he or she remained on a section 3. The present law is quite clear, however, that a section 3 cannot be renewed if the patient no longer needs to be in hospital and cannot be enforced just to ensure that there is cooperation with medication.

This highlights one of the major problems in the treatment of schizophrenia. Many patients agree to have their medication when they know they are on a section, but may well abruptly stop it, with disastrous consequences, when the section expires.

Section 136 – place of safety order

The police may take someone whom they find in a public place and whom they have good reason to suspect of suffering from mental illness and to be in immediate need of care and control to a 'place of safety'. This can be a hospital or other place for the mentally disordered or, in exceptional circumstances, a police station. This enables an assessment to be made by a doctor and an approved social worker. Unless another form of detention order is made, the patient may be kept for no more than 72 hours.

Section 135 – right of access order

This section enables a magistrate to issue a warrant for access to the home of someone who is considered to be mentally ill and who, because of these problems, is in danger of serious neglect, ill-treatment or other dangers such as starvation, setting the home alight, hypothermia and so on. Under these cirumstances, a police constable accompanied by a doctor and an approved social worker is enabled to enter the home; the doctor will then be able to advise whether the patient should be removed to a place of safety, pending an application for a section.

MENTAL HEALTH REVIEW TRIBUNALS

Each of the regional health authorities in the UK is covered by a separate mental health review tribunal (MHRT). A patient detained under section 2 may appeal to them against detention within the first 14 days, those on section 3 in the first six months. These appeals are heard as soon as possible by a tribunal of three members – a legal member who acts as president, a lay member who is usually someone with experience of work with the mentally ill, and a consultant psychiatrist who makes a preliminary examination of the patient prior to the tribunal sitting. A patient under section 3 who does not appeal is automatically referred to them after 6 months detention.

The patient may present his own case but is entitled to be represented by a solicitor, legal aid being available if necessary, and evidence is heard from the responsible medical officer, the approved social worker and any other witnesses, such as relatives, who wish to be present. The solicitor may also call for a further independent psychiatric opinion if it appears to be warranted.

The tribunal has wide powers, but endeavours to conduct its

proceedings on as informal a basis as possible. They must discharge the patient from the section if the criteria of the Act are not met. They can also order delayed discharge from hospital, recommend leave of absence or transfer to another hospital. Relatives can speak to the tribunal in the absence of the patient if they wish, although it is usually considered to be best for the patient to know what is being said. All the discussions are completely confidential and tribunals act as a valuable safeguard both for the patient and relatives.

GUARDIANSHIP

A guardianship order requires the patient to live in a specified place, to attend for the purposes of medical treatment, education or training and to allow access by a doctor, approved social worker or other persons specified by the guardian. The guardian may be a relative, a friend or the local authority social services department. Application can be made by the nearest relative or an approved social worker with the agreement of the relative, and recommendations by two doctors are required. A guardianship order lasts initially for six months, but then can be renewed. There is also a right of appeal to the MHRT for those in guardianship.

Guardianship may have some place in certain cases of schizophrenia where negative symptoms of apathy, self neglect and emotional withdrawal predominate; for example, it can be used to discourage the patient from sleeping rough or living with those who might exploit him. However, there are obvious difficulties in enforcement where a patient resists the guardianship order and is non-compliant.

CONSENT TO TREATMENT

All patients must give informed consent to a treatment in schizophrenic illness, usually neuroleptic medication, and in the case of a detained patient the responsible medical officer must issue a certificate to say that the patient has consented.

If the patient does not consent, or is too ill to understand the nature of the treatment, the doctor, after consideration of alternative therapies, can ask the **Mental Health Commission** to send an appointed doctor for a second opinion. He or she will visit the patient, discuss the plan of treatment and decide whether the treatment should be given.

Certificate of consent to treatment

Form 38

Mental Health Act 1983
Section 58 (3) (a)

I

(full name and address)

delete the phrase which does not apply

the responsible medical officer

a registered medical practitioner appointed for the purposes of Part IV of the Act,

certify that

(full name and address of patient)

(a) is capable of understanding the nature, purpose and likely effects of

(give description of treatment or plan of treatment)

AND

(b) has consented to that treatment.

Signed _____ Date _____

Printed in the UK for HMSO Dd 8405938 6/83 (11037)

A Consent to Treatment Certificate.

MENTAL HEALTH ACT COMMISSION

This Commission has been set up by the Secretary of State for Health, and its membership includes lawyers, nurses, psychologists, social workers and laymen, in roughly equal numbers, with a larger number of doctors who have more duties in spheres such as consent to treatment.

The role of the Commission is to watch over the interests of detained patients. The commissioners visit hospitals and interview such patients, investigating any complaints by them or their relatives. It is also involved with maintaining a code of practice which covers treatment for mental disorders in general. Its functions are quite separate from those of the mental health review tribunal and it has no power to discharge a patient.

NEAREST RELATIVE

The nearest relative may often be involved in seeking admission for a patient under the Mental Health Act. Some are naturally reluctant to do so, fearing that the patient will be bitterly resentful against them, and preferring to leave the application to a social worker. Nearest relatives can also make an order for discharge from a section or guardianship, although, in exceptional cases, the responsible medical officer can block this if he feels there are particularly severe hazards.

The nearest relatives for such purposes are firstly a husband or wife, then a son or daughter, followed by a father or mother and brother or sister. If a patient has two relatives of equal standing (for example father and mother), the elder takes precedence. A cohabitee can also act as nearest relative if they have been living with the patient for not less than six months, although such a person does not have precedence over a legal spouse unless there has been a separation or desertion. If a person is usually living with, or cared for, by one or more relatives or persons acting as such, they will take precedence over others.

RIGHTS OF PATIENTS

Every detained patient must be given a copy of their rights when admitted to hospital, including details of how to appeal against their sections. The visits of mental health commissioners must also be publicised, and patients can request a private interview with them.

CRIMINAL PROCEEDINGS

Serious criminal proceedings for those suffering with a schizophrenic illness are, fortunately, comparatively rare. Offences such as shoplifting, loitering with intent, disturbances of the peace and impulsive acts such as smashing windows usually occur in response to delusions and hallucinations. A psychiatric opinion can be sought by the defending solicitor or requested by the court and an order made for psychiatric treatment either as an outpatient or an inpatient.

Publicity has recently been given to the fact that shortage of accommodation in hospitals has led to some mentally ill offenders having to be sent to prison. This should never be allowed to happen; there can be no worse environment for someone with a schizophrenic illness than to be confined in such conditions. It is vital that hospital beds remain available for anyone who commits a criminal offence due to a psychiatric problem and who needs inpatient care.

11

SCHIZOPHRENIA IN ART AND LITERATURE

The concept of schizophrenia as an illness which has affected individuals in all cultures and at all times in history is reinforced by the descriptions of it in historical documents and in literature. The Greek physicians such as Hippocrates, who were so ahead of their time in recognising the indivisibility of mind and body, included in their case histories descriptions of conditions which would appear to be schizophrenic. Saul, who in 1025 BC became the first king of Israel, according to the Bible underwent a change of personality characteristic of a psychotic disturbance. It is recorded that his character altered and he became suspicious, irritable, mournful and unpredictable. Interestingly, those around thought he would be soothed by music and David, the future king, was appointed to play for him.

SCHIZOPHRENIA IN LITERATURE

In *Hamlet* Shakespeare portrayed the tragedy of Ophelia, who would seem to have the classical symptoms of schizophrenia. After witnessing the murder of her father by Hamlet and his rejection of her, she becomes acutely mentally ill. She is described as speaking things in half sense so that those around cannot understand her, although they feel that there might be some thought in her utterances. Covering herself with fantastic garlands of 'crow flowers, nettles, daisies and long purples', she falls into a stream, singing sadly, is dragged down by the water and drowns. Both Othello and Lady Macbeth are perceptive studies of mental disintegration, the first from jealousy and the second from guilt.

It is obvious that Shakespeare had made some observations about how the mentally ill were treated. In *Twelfth Night* when Malvolio appears bizarrely dressed, as he thinks to please Olivia, he is regarded as mentally ill and confined to a darkened cell to be tormented. In *King Lear* Edgar disguises himself as 'Bedlam beggar', that is a wandering schizophrenic, in the guise of poor Tom. One of the symptoms that he pretends to have are auditory hallucinations; he claims that there is a foul fiend that haunts him in the voice of a nightingale.

One of the best known portraits of what was undoubtedly a schizophrenic illness is in Charlotte Bronte's *Jane Eyre*. The unfortunate Mrs Rochester has become mentally ill and is confined to a room at the top of the house. She is given to rather melodramatic nocturnal wanderings and finally burns the house down, killing herself and injuring Mr Rochester, who appears to have little concept of how to treat someone who is psychiatrically unwell. Perhaps he cannot be blamed too much, since studies of the time indicate that such confinement was not an uncommon way for respectable families to treat a member who had become unbalanced. One wonders also about the diagnosis of Catherine in Emily Bronte's *Wuthering Heights*, who goes into both a physical and mental decline when she realises that her marriage has made it impossible for her to continue her relationship with Heathcliff. She alternates between anger and tearfulness and rushes out into the coldness of the moors, scantily dressed, regardless of any considerations for her health. She is described as pulling feathers from the pillow and arranging them on the sheet according to their different species; all of these have a special significance for her according to the bird from which they came. It is possible that her mental anguish has induced an acute schizophrenic breakdown.

The Northamptonshire poet John Clare (1793–1864) suffered from periodic episodes of schizophrenia which necessitated admission to the local asylum. Most of his poetry was written before he became mentally ill with a paranoid psychosis in 1837, but he has left us with a moving account of his distress at the realisation that his illness was returning and his awareness that he would soon be once again taken from his home.

A number of modern novelists and playwrights have been interested in the borderline between sanity and mental disturbance, and some have realistic portraits of schizophrenia in their books, possibly based upon their own personal experience of the illness. We have already mentioned Septimus in Virginia Woolf's *Mrs Dalloway*. In *Tender is the Night* the American novelist Scott Fitzgerald describes the progress of a schizophrenic illness in the young wife of a doctor. Similarly, the playwright Tennessee Williams, whose sister Rose had a severe schizophrenic breakdown, brings the illness and its treatment into a number of his plays.

The Rake's Progress by Hogarth.

SCHIZOPHRENIA IN ART

Hogarth (1697–1764) has shown us what it was like to be in Bedlam at the time. In his study of the Rake, this profligate man ends up in Bedlam. It is a scene of horror, in which all the mentally ill are depicted: these include the man who has grandiose delusions wearing his royal crown, the apathetic man staring blankly into space, and the religious fanatic with his Bible. The rake is in irons, a means of physical restraint common in those days, which are only taken off when he collapses. In contrast, two elegant people who have known him in his better days are visiting to see the sights.

A number of artists have had schizophrenic breakdowns. Probably the most famous is Vincent van Gogh who became mentally ill in 1888, broken by poverty and his frantic absorption in his art. He could scarcely sell a picture, began to experience auditory hallucinations and had a series of break-downs, during one of which he cut off his ear.

Self-portrait of Vincent van Gogh.

SCHIZOPHRENIA IN HISTORY

That schizophrenia can affect anyone is illustrated by the number of notable people who have suffered from it. Ludwig II of Bavaria, who formed an intense friendship with Wagner the composer, began to believe he was an incarnation of Lohengrin, a Germanic legendary figure, and built the famous castles in which he acted out his delusional beliefs. On winter nights he would take wild drives round the countryside with all his servants dressed in the style of Louis XIV. He chose to go around at night because he had decided to reverse night and day, having a moon painted on his bedroom ceiling and being rowed around the lake in the darkness dressed as he thought Lohengrin might have been.

Nijinsky, the famous Russian dancer, sadly developed a schizophrenic illness quite early in his life. He suffered from delusions of persecution and spent the rest of his life in hospitals and clinics. Sometimes the staff and patients would see glimpses of his old genius when he attempted to dance for them.

12

THE FUTURE

MEDICAL RESEARCH

There is every reason for optimism. One of the most exciting pieces of news is that of the possibility that a genetic link has been isolated. Research workers at the Middlesex Hospital have examined fragments of genetic material from groups of families, each of which had a schizophrenic member. They then looked for a particular gene – a single unit of genetic information – which was unique to those who had the disease, and now believe that they may have discovered one, although this still remains to be established.

The importance of this discovery lies not so much in being able to predict who will develop schizophrenia, since only a relatively small number of cases of schizophrenia have a family history of the illness, but in exploring the ways in which the gene may exert its influence. It is possible that what we now label as schizophrenia may well be a group of illnesses; it is of interest to speculate, for example, upon what causes one person to make a complete recovery and another to continue to have symptoms. The genetic research may well provide a clue to this and to an underlying biochemical abnormality.

PUBLIC UNDERSTANDING

Moreover, schizophrenia is now becoming an illness where there is much greater public understanding and interest. I have been interested, while preparing this book, to discover how many people who learn about it tell me of a family member or a friend who has had a schizophrenic breakdown. And they have all wished to know more so that they could help.

It is only when there is public awareness of the distress that this condition can cause that there will be an increased impetus to carry out research. In the past schizophrenics and their families have tended to be an isolated and forgotten group, but this is no longer the case.

At the same time, those who are ill should not be forgotten. Pressure has to be exerted to ensure that they have as rich a life as possible, that they have adequate accommodation and work facilities and continue to benefit from advances in treatment.

GLOSSARY

Aetiology Causation.

Akathisia A feeling of restlessness making it difficult to keep still.

Amphetamines A group of drugs previously used mainly because of their control of appetite. They have a transitory stimulant effect which is often followed by a rebound depression, they are habit forming and can produce a paranoid delusional illness.

Anaemia A condition in which there is a lack of adequately functioning red blood cells. Since the function of these cells is to transmit oxygen around the body to the tissues, a deficiency leads to symptoms such as tiredness and breathlessness.

Anxiety A feeling of uneasiness as if something unpleasant is about to happen. A normal reaction to stress, but becomes a problem when it persists after the stress is over.

Apathy A feeling of indifference to people and things in the environment

Biochemistry The study of the chemical processes involved in living organisms.

Carbohydrates Food substances such as starch and sugar.

Catatonia A condition in which the individual withdraws and will stand or lie in one position without moving for an abnormal length of time.

Cerebral hemispheres The higher centres of the brain which deal with thought and emotion.

Cerebrospinal fluid The fluid which flows around the ventricles of the brain and the spinal cord and act as a buffer for the central nervous system.

Cortisone A hormone manufactured by the adrenal glands in

135

the body, but also produced synthetically. Used as an anti-inflammatory agent in the treatment of conditions such as rheumatoid arthritis.

Delusion   A fixed false belief which cannot be altered by any appeal to logic or reasoning and which is alien to the individual's cultural background and intelligence.

Depot   A preparation which, when injected in quantity into the tissues, is released into the bloodstream in gradual amounts over a period of time.

Depression   A feeling of profound sadness or in more severe cases a complete loss of interest, often accompanied by physical symptoms such as poor sleep and loss of appetite.

Diabetes   A condition in which, due to a lack of insulin (a hormone produced in the pancreas) the body cannot deal with sugar.

Double bind   A psychological state in which one individual puts another into a situation where he or she receives a message to do one thing whilst the expectation is that he or she will do the opposite. An example would be the mother who ostensibly tells her child she wants him or her to be independent, whilst assuming a role which makes the child unable to leave her.

Dystonia   A condition where the muscles become fixed in abnormal attitudes.

Elation   A feeling of extreme happiness and well being.

Enzyme   A substance which produces chemical reactions in living cells.

Epidemiology   The study of the way in which diseases occur in the community.

Genes   The units of inheritance which give individuals their unique characteristics.

Gluten   A protein contained in wheat and other cereal grains.

Hallucination   A false perception of something which is not present in reality in the external world.

Hallucinogenic   A substance which produces hallucinations.

Hereditary   Transmitted from one generation to another by means of the genes; this accounts for all normal characteristics such as height, sex, eye and hair colour as well as any tendency to disease.

Hysteria   A neurotic condition in which anxiety and stress lead to a physical state such as paralysis or blindness without there being an associated physical disease to cause it.

Illusion   A false perception of a real sensory stimulus.

Mania   A condition of excessive excitement, the opposite of depression, associated with hyperactivity and sleeplessness.

Mental subnormality   A condition where there is impaired development of the mind associated with a failure to develop normal intelligence.

Multiple sclerosis   A disease of unknown causation associated with a loss of the myelin sheath around the nerves, resulting in symptoms such as incoordination and muscle weakness.

Neologism   A new word.

Neuroleptic   A term applied to drugs which have an effect upon cerebral functioning.

Neurosis   A psychiatric disorder in which normal patterns of behaviour are exaggerated so that they become incapacitating, but where the individual remains in contact with reality.

Neurotransmitter   A chemical messenger in the central nervous system.

Obesity   The state of being overweight.

Obsession   A persistent thought or act which an individual is unable to fight against, e.g. a constant desire to wash the hands.

Organic   Something which affects the structure of an organ.

Paranoid   Having feelings of being persecuted.

Parkinsonism   A condition of the central nervous system where there is shaking of the limbs, slowness in movements and a mask-like facial expression.

Personality   The sum total of those characteristics which make up an individual.

Psychiatry   The study of mental illness and abnormal behaviour.

Psychoanalysis   A specialised form of psychotherapy.

Psychology   The study of normal behaviour.

Psychopathic   A personality disorder characterised by persistent antisocial behaviour and an absence of remorse.

Psychosis   A psychiatric illness which affects the entire personality and where there is a loss of contact with reality.

Psychosomatic   A physical condition such as a peptic ulcer, asthma or skin rash produced by stress and exacerbated by it.

Psychotherapy   Discussion and exploration of the reasons behind an individual's behaviour.

Puerperium   The period immediately following childbirth.

Retardation   A slowing up of the mental and physical

processes.

Rheumatoid arthritis A condition producing widespread inflammation and deformity of the joints.

Schizoid A personality characteristic describing someone who is withdrawn and solitary.

Tardive dyskinesia A side-effect of the neuroleptic drugs where there is involuntary repetitive movements of the limbs, trunk and face.

Tranquillisers Drugs, such as Valium and Librium, which tranquillise the mind.

Twins *identical* Formed by division of *one* fertilised egg and have identical genetic characteristics.

non-identical formed by the fertilisation of two separate eggs and having the same genetic characteristics as a normal brother and sister but developing in the womb at the same time.

Ventricles The pathways in the brain through which the cerebrospinal fluid flows.

Volition Exercise of will.

Zygote The fertilised egg produced from the fusion of ovum and sperm which will divide to produce the embryo.

USEFUL ADDRESSES

Department of Health and Social Security
The Department publishes a number of useful leaflets, all of which can be obtained from your local DHSS office. In case of difficulty, write to:
Leaflets Unit
PO Box 21
Stanmore
Middlesex HA7 1AY
In addition there is a free telephone service to get information about social security benefits:
0800 666555

Mental After Care Association
Eagle House
110 Jermyn Street
London SW1Y 6HB
01-839 5953
Provides homes and hostels for adults in the south-east recovering from mental illness.

MIND – National Association for Mental Health
22 Harley Street
London W1N 2ED
01-637-0741

National Schizophrenia Fellowship
78 Victoria Road
Surbiton
Surrey KT6 4NS
01-390 3651
The NSF publish numerous books and pamphlets which are obtainable from the above address.

197 King's Cross Road
London WC1X 9BZ
01-837 6436
Serves Greater London and as a base for the VOICES Forum.

9 St Michaels Court
Victoria Street
West Bromwich B70 8ET
021-500 5988

47 Rosemary Street
Belfast BT1 1QB
0232 248006

Drop-In Centre
3A Lower Catherine Street
Newry
County Down

Mr Steve Forge
29 Balmoral Road
St Andrews
Bristol BS7 9AX
0272 245140
Temporary Development Officer (working from home)

40 Shandwick Place
Edinburgh EH2 4RT
031 226 2025

Mrs Faith Feak (Co-ordinator)
5 St Georges Esplanade
St Peter Port
Guernsey
0481 22589

Mrs Marion Harrison (Chairman)
Clos du Saie
Rozel
Jersey
Channel Islands
0534 51244

38 Collingwood Buildings
Collingwood Street
Newcastle upon Tyne NE1 1JH
091 261 4343

17 Oxford Street
Southampton
Hampshire SO1 1DJ
0703 225664

Other staffed offices

Birmingham Relatives' Centre
Rooms 88-89
191 Corporation Street
Birmingham B4 6SE
021-236 4286

Chesterfield Group Office
Unit 19
Boythorpe Depot
Central Avenue
Chesterfield
Derbyshire
0246 232465

Surrey Group Office
9 Queen Street
Godalming
Surrey GU7 1BA
04868 5950

Other organisations

North West Fellowship
48 Allen Street
Warrington WA2 7JB
0925 571680

Psychiatric Rehabilitation Association
The Groupwork Centre
21A Kingsland High Street
Dalston
London E8 2JS
01-254 9753
Provides community care in north and east London.

SANE (Schizophrenia: A National Emergency)
120 Regent Street,
London W1A 5FE
01-434 0150

Schizophrenia Association of Great Britain
International Schizophrenia Centre
Bryn Hyfryd
The Crescent
Bangor
Gwynedd LLS7 2AG
0248 334048

Schizophrenia Association of Ireland
4 Fitzwilliam Place
Dublin 2
Ireland
Dublin 761988

FURTHER READING

SCHIZOPHRENIA IN FICTION

Charlotte Bronte, *Jane Eyre*.
Jean Rhys, *The Wide Sargasso Sea*. This takes the character
Mrs Rochester from *Jane Eyre* and looks at her early life
in the West Indies and how she came to England.
F. Scott Fitzgerald, *Tender is the Night*.
Virginia Woolf, *Mrs Dalloway*.
Evelyn Waugh, *The Ordeal of Gilbert Pinfold*. This book
describes the effects of hallucinations due to alcohol
withdrawal, rather than schizophrenia.

NON-FICTION

Katia Gilhome Herbst (ed.), *Schizophrenia: A Briefing for
all those concerned with the Treatment and Care of
Schizophrenia*, The Mental Health Foundation, 1987
(distributed by the National Schizophrenia Fellowship).
R. Hunter and I. McAlpine, *A History of Psychiatry*. A big
book for anyone interested in how psychiatry
developed.
R.D. Laing, *The Divided Self*, Penguin. A psychoanalytic
view of schizophrenia and schizophrenic thinking.
Sir Martin Roth and Jerome Kroll, *The Reality of Mental
Illness*, Cambridge University Press, 1987. A reply to
Thomas Ssasz's book.
Thomas Ssasz, *The Myth of Mental Illness*. An American
psychoanalyst questions our whole concept of what is

mental illness.

Diet books
Rita Greer, *Gluten Free Cookery*, Thorsons.
Gwen Howe, *Schizophrenia. A Fresh Approach*, David and
  Charles. Discusses many aspects of schizophrenia and
  dietary management in particular.
Dr Peter Rawcliffe and Ruth Rolph SRD, *The Gluten-Free
  Diet Book*, Macdonald Optima, Positive Health Guides.
Elizabeth Workman SRD, Dr John Hunter and Dr Virginia
  Alun Jones, *The Allergy Diet*, Macdonald Optima,
  Positive Health Guides.

INDEX

abortion, 110
activity, changes in, 41
acupuncture, 83
acute onset, 49–51
additives, food, 80
adolescence, 21–2
age, risk factors, 39
akathisia, 64
alcohol, 104–5
alternative therapies, 82–3
amphetamines, 30, 36, 39, 55
anaemia, 55
anti-depressant drugs, 65
anxiety, 13, 58
appearance, preoccupation with, 41
appetite suppressant drugs, 66, 105
art: schizophrenia in, 129–31; therapy, 78
assessment, 47–55, 120–21
attendance allowance, 95, 96–7
auditory hallucinations, 20

behaviour modification, 78–9
behavioural problems, 42
benefit system, 93–100
benzedrine, 30
biochemical factors, 30–1
birth control, 111
Bleuler, Eugen, 5

brain: dopamine, 30–1; organic factors in schizophrenia, 31–2, 68
breastfeeding, 111
Bronte, Charlotte, 128
Bronte, Emily, 128
budgeting loans, 98

caffeine, 80
cannabis, 36, 55
cars, driving, 106
catatonic stupor, 26, 82
causes of schizophrenia, 27–35
central nervous system: biochemical factors, 30–1; drugs and, 63–1; organic factors in schizophrenia, 31–2, 68
childbirth, 31–2, 36, 40, 109, 110–11
children, 108–11, 116
chlorpromazine, 59, 60–1
cigarettes, 105
Clare, John, 33, 128–9
classification, 25–6
clinical psychologists, 91
clinics, community, 86–7, 88, 104
Clopixol, 59, 61
coeliac disease, 79
coffee, 80

community care, 9, 25, 85–91
community care grants, 98
community clinics, 86–7, 88, 104
community psychiatric nurses, 90
compulsory admission to hospital, 116–17, 119–22, 125
computerised tomography (CT) scanning, 31–2
concentration, loss of, 40–1
Connolly, John, 6–7, 24
consent to treatment, 123–4
contraception, 111
cortisone, 30, 40, 55
counselling, 70–1
criminal proceeedings, 126

David, King of Israel, 127
day hospitals, 85–6
delusions, 18–19, 42, 48–9, 115–16
Department of Social Security see DSS
Depixol, 59, 61
depot preparations, 61–2, 65
depression, 13–14, 41, 114–15
depressive delusions, 18
dexedrine, 30
DSS, 97, 98, 99, 100
diagnosis, 39–44, 54–5
diet, 79–81, 107
Disipal, 63
dizziness, 63
Dolmatil, 59, 61
dopamine, 30–1, 63
'double-bind' phenomena, 33
drinking, 104–5
driving, 106
Droleptan, 59
drop-in centres, 86
droperidol, 59

drowsiness, 63
drugs: anti-depressants, 65; and breastfeeding, 111; depot preparations, 61–2, 65; hallucinogenic, 30, 36–7 39; illegal, 22, 36–7, 55, 105 lithium, 65; neuroleptic, 57–65; during pregnancy, 109; psychotropic, 57–65; risk factors, 39, 40, 55; sedatives, 66; side-effects, 63–5; sleeping tablets, 66; stopping, 62–3; and travel, 105–6
dystonia, 64

early signs, 40–3
education, 101–2
electroconvulsive therapy (ECT), 81–2
emergency admissions to hospital, 120
emotions, 25; emotional changes, 17, 42–3, 65; expressed emotion (EE), 34–5, 74
employment see work
environmental factors, 33–5
expressed emotion (EE), 34–5 74

faintness, 63
families: and compulsory admission to hospital, 125; family history, 28–9, 40; family therapy, 73–6; living with schizophrenia, 113–17
feeling, disturbances of, 17
Fentazin, 59
Fitzgerald, F. Scott, 129
flupenthixol, 59, 61
fluphenazine decanoate, 60, 61

fluphenazine enanthate, 60
fluspirilene, 60
food additives, 80
Freud, Sigmund, 8, 66

genetic factors, 28–9, 108, 133
George III, King, 6
gluten-free diet, 79–80
grandiose delusions, 18
grants, community care, 98
group homes, 89
group therapy, 72–3
guardianship orders, 123

Haldol, 59, 61
hallucinations, 20–1, 43
hallucinogenic drugs, 30, 36–7,
 39
haloperidol, 59, 60, 61
hearing defects, 40
hebephrenic schizophrenia, 26
Hippocrates, 127
history, 5–9, 127, 131
Hogarth, William, 129–30
homeopathy, 82–3
hospital treatment, 45, 47;
 compulsory admission,
 116–17, 119–22, 125; day
 hospitals, 85–6; inpatient
 care, 85; long-term care,
 88–9, 90; rights of patients,
 125; travel costs, 99
hostels, 89, 90
housing benefit, 99
hypnosis, 83
hypochondria, 43

incidence, 14
income support, 97–8, 99
industrial therapy units, 87–8
infections, risk factors, 39
inherited factors, 28–9, 108,
 133

injections, depot preparations.
 61–2, 65
insurance, travel, 106
Integrin, 59
invalid care allowance (ICA),
 97
invalidity benefit, 94–5, 99

Kemadrin, 63

Largactil, 59, 61, 63
laws, 119–26
leisure activities, 104–6
Librium, 58
literature, schizophrenia in,
 112–13, 127–9
lithium, 65
living with schizophrenia,
 101–17
loans, budgeting, 98
loneliness, 69–70
long-term care, 88–9
LSD, 30, 36–7, 39, 55
Ludwig II, King of Bavaria,
 131

manic-depressive psychosis,
 13–14, 65
'marital skew' phenomena,
 32–3
marriage, 107–8, 111–13
Matthews, Mr, 6–7
medication see drugs
Melleril, 60, 61,63
Mental Health Act (1983), 91,
 119–22, 125
Mental Health Act
 Commission, 123–5
Mental Health Review
 Tribunals, 122–3, 125
mental hospitals, 5–9, 88
mescaline, 30

metabolic disorders, 30–1
methotrimeprazine, 60
Middlesex Hospital, 133
MIND, 86, 89–90, 101
Modecate, 60, 61
Moditen, 60
mood changes, 17, 65
mouth, dryness, 63
movement, disturbances of, 21
muscles, side-effects of drugs, 63–4

National Association for Mental Health (MIND), 86, 89–90, 101
National Insurance contributions, 93–9
National Schizophrenic Fellowship, 101, 104
neologisms, 16
Neulactil, 60
neuroleptic drugs, 23, 30, 57–65
neuroses, 11–13
Nijinsky, 131
nurses, community, 90

obesity, 80, 107; drugs to control, 66, 105
obsessions, 13
onset of schizophrenia, 49–54
Orap, 60, 61
orphenadrine, 63
oxypertine, 59

painting, 78
paranoid schizophrenia, 6–7, 18, 26
paraphrenia, 23
Parkinsonism, 30, 63–4
passivity, feelings of, 16
patients, rights, 125

pericyazine, 60
perphenazine, 59
personality, 29, 39, 69
phenylketonuria, 30
phobias, 13
pimozide, 60, 61
Pinel, 5–6
Piportil, 60
pipothiazine palmitate, 60
place of safety orders, 121–2
pregnancy, 109–10
procyclidine, 63
promazine, 60
psychiatrists, 91
psychological factors, 32–3
psychologists, 91
psychoses, 13–14
psychotherapy, 66–70
psychotropic drugs, 24, 57–65
public awareness, 133–4

Redeptin, 60
rehabilitation units, 76–7
relatives, 125
relaxation techniques, 83
research, 133
rights of patients, 125
risk factors, 39–40

La Salpétrière asylum, 5–6
Saul, King of Israel, 127
'schizoid' personality, 29, 39
schizophrenia: assessment, 47–55, 120–1; causes, 27–35; classification, 25–6; diagnosis, 39–44, 54–5; onset of, 21–4, 49–54; outlook, 24–5; prevention, 35–7; symptoms, 15–21; treatment, 57–83
Schizophrenic Association of Great Britain, 79

sedatives, 66
Serenace, 60
severe disablement allowance (SDA), 95–6, 97, 99
Shakespeare, William, 127–8
sheltered workshops, 88
sickness benefit, 94, 99
sickness certificates, 93
side-effects, drugs, 63–5
simple schizophrenia, 26
sleeping tablets, 66
smell, hallucinations, 21
smoking, 105
social therapies, 76–8
social workers, 91
Sparine, 60
statutory sick pay (SSP), 93, 99
Stelazine, 60, 61
steroids, 30
stress, 22–3, 25, 34–5, 40, 69
suicidal ideas, 114–15
sulpiride, 59, 61
supervised lodgings, 89
surgery, risk factors, 39
symptoms, 15–21

tactile hallucinations, 20
tardive dyskinisia, 64
taste, hallucinations, 21
television, 16–17
thioridazine, 60, 61
thought disturbances, 15–17, 42
tranquillisers, 23, 30, 58
travel, 105–6
travel costs, 99
treatment, 57–83; alternative therapies, 82–3; consent to, 123–4; counselling, 70–1; diet, 79–81; drugs, 57–66; electroconvulsive therapy (ECT), 81–2; family therapy, 73–6; group therapy, 72–3; Mental Health Act, 121; psychotherapy, 66–70; social therapies, 76–8
trifluoperazine, 60, 61
twins, 28
Type I schizophrenia, 26
Type II schizophrenia, 26

unemployment pay, 97

Valium, 58
Van Gogh, Vincent, 33, 78, 130
Veractil, 60
violent behaviour, 19, 46, 116
visual defects, 40
visual hallucinations, 20
vitamin deficiency, 55, 79
'voices', 20, 43
volition, disorders of, 21

weight gain, 80, 107; drugs to control, 66, 105
welfare benefits, 93–100
wheat gluten, 79–80
Williams, Tennessee, 129
withdrawal from social contact, 40, 113–14
Woolf, Virginia, 112–13, 129
work, 102–3; industrial therapy units, 87–8; rehabilitation units, 76–7; sheltered workshops, 88

yoga, 83

zuclopenthixol, 59, 61

MORE BOOKS FROM OPTIMA

Positive Health Guides

The Positive Health Guides series has long been recognised as one of the most authoritative lists of health books published. The books have all been written by experts in their field to provide accessible, well-presented information on a variety of illnesses and ailments, for the general reader.

The Allergy Diet by Elizabeth Workman SRD, Dr John Hunter and Dr Virginia Alun Jones
ISBN 0 356 14458 5, price £5.99
The Allergy Diet, based on extensive research done on food intolerance at Addenbrooke's Hospital, Cambridge, provides full and accessible information on the subject plus a step-by-step diet plan. There is also a comprehensive listing of food additives to avoid, together with their E numbers, and 150 recipes ensure both good nutrition and exciting variety while testing for the 'culprit' in your diet.

Anxiety and Depression by Professor Robert Priest
ISBN 0 356 14460 7, price £5.99
Professor Robert Priest has written this book to reassure and provide help for those people who feel anxious and depressed. In particular, he covers practical self-help measures to reduce stress, an explanation of the causes and effects of anxiety and depression, and information on the professional help available to sufferers.

Caring for an Elderly Relative by Dr Keith Thompson
ISBN 0 356 14465 8, price £5.99
In this sympathetic guide, helpful advice from a family doctor and geriatrician explains how you can decide whether home care is best for your relative; adapt your home to suit an elderly person; give the right care in health and sickness; find out about community support and look after yourself as well.

Most important, Dr Keith Thompson shows you how to keep your perspective as he answers your questions about ageing.

Caring for an Elderly Relative is fully illustrated with photographs and diagrams explaining common illness and home nursing techniques.

The Food Intolerance Diet Book by Elizabeth Workman SRD, Dr John Hunter and Dr Virginia Alun Jones
ISBN 0 356 14453 4, price £4.99
Written by the authors of the bestseller *The Allergy Diet,* this book contains research information on many conditions caused by food intolerance, plus 150 delicious recipes and a useful shopping guide.

The Gluten-Free Diet Book by Dr Peter Rawcliffe and Ruth Rolph SRD
ISBN 0 356 14487 9, price £4.99
This book explains how to eliminate gluten, which is responsible for coeliac disease, from the diet. It gives sound advice on how to avoid common foods containing gluten, and how to organise and adapt to a balanced and healthy gluten-free diet.

Stress and Relaxation by Jane Madders
ISBN 0 356 14504 2, price £5.99
Relaxation is an excellent way of dealing with the stresses of modern life. Jane Madders, who has taught stress-management for over 40 years, describes in this book numerous relaxation techniques which can help everyone to counteract stress and lead a healthier life.

All Optima books are available at your bookshop or newsagent, or can be ordered from the following address:

Optima, Cash Sales Department,
PO Box 11, Falmouth, Cornwall TR10 9EN

Please send a cheque or postal order (no currency), and allow 60p for postage and packing for the first book, plus 25p for the second book and 15p for each additional book ordered up to a maximum of £1.90 in the UK.

Customers in Eire and BFPO please allow 60p for the first book, 25p for the second book plus 15p per copy for the next 7 books, thereafter 9p per book.

Overseas customers please allow £1.25 for postage and packing for the first book and 28p per copy for each additional book.